Contents

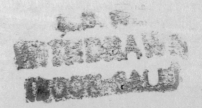

Cholesterol and Your Health

Hardening of the arteries (arteriosclerosis), hypertension (high blood pressure) and coronary heart disease are amongst the biggest killers in Western society.

Most of us know of friends, family, neighbours, work colleagues or acquaintances who have died young, often in their 40s or 50s, without warning. Here today, gone tomorrow – leaving behind a devastated family and a sense of waste – so much to live for … And yet how much notice do we give to whether we are doing the same things which led them (at least in part) to early death?

We all know of older individuals who have become limited in their activities, unable to carry on a normal life or perform normal tasks, due to health problems linked to heart or circulatory problems – high blood pressure, angina, stroke, coronary heart disease etc. Not all of these conditions have high cholesterol as their only cause, but chances are it is a key feature, and in many instances the main feature of what has contributed to their condition.

Circulatory Damage

Atherosclerosis occurs when plaque – a mixture of blood platelets, fatty substances, cholesterol and calcium – is laid down as a protective repair to the inner lining of arteries. The damage itself is thought to be caused by the action of free radicals – which are discussed in Chapter 2 (*see page 12*). The plaque hardens on the inner lining of the arteries causing narrowing and, at worst, actual blockages. Detailed studies of people living in countries where the incidence of these conditions is highest and where it is lowest have shown a definite link between high levels of cholesterol in the blood and the onset of such diseases. When there are high levels of cholesterol in the blood, the arteries are more likely to develop obstructions which slow down blood flow to the heart, kidneys, brain, legs etc. Fatty deposits may form in the arteries, clogging them, with the likelihood of cerebrovascular (brain circulation) and cardiac problems developing.

High blood pressure is often the next stage, as the heart struggles to pump blood around blood vessels which are getting narrower all the time.

This constant effort stresses the heart and the blood vessels, depriving the tissues of fresh oxygenated blood, creating a whole new set of problems such as intermittent claudication, where walking becomes painful and difficult. Research also suggests that high cholesterol levels contribute to gallstones and colon cancer, as well as impotence.

Different Countries, Different Diets and Different Diseases

Research has been conducted into the eating habits of the nations that typically have low cholesterol levels (Japan, China and the Mediterranean) to see whether the reasons for the protection they seem to enjoy, from heart disease and some forms of cancer for example, is partially due to what they eat – and just such a connection has been found. It has been discovered that eating foods rich in fats and cholesterol does increase levels of cholesterol in the blood, but this is only part of the story.

It has also been discovered that, despite the connection between diet and cholesterol levels, around three quarters of our cholesterol is manufactured by our own bodies (mainly in the liver). So if only about a quarter of the body's cholesterol comes from the food you eat, does this mean that you need not worry about how much cholesterol-rich food you eat?

Good and Bad Cholesterol

There are a number of answers to that question – with the short answer being no – if you want to get cholesterol to a safe level, you cannot ignore what you eat as a cause, for several reasons.

1) It does matter how much cholesterol-rich food you eat because not only the amount of cholesterol in the bloodstream matters – but the type of cholesterol (there is a 'good' and a 'bad' type) is important and we need to

examine what this means in more detail later in this chapter. At this stage just remember that 'bad' cholesterol comes largely from your diet.

2) What you eat also matters because a diet which is rich in fat and simple carbohydrates (sugars and refined flours for example) creates a situation which makes your body manufacture too much cholesterol, so adding to the burden. How this happens will also be explained, so that when it comes to choosing foods from the rich variety that is safe and health promoting, you will know the reasons why.

What is Cholesterol?

Cholesterol is an absolutely vital part of the economy of your body. You cannot live without it. It is more of a waxy substance – known as a sterol – rather than a fat, although it is very much associated with fats. Just like fats, cholesterol is not easy to dissolve in blood plasma (blood consists of plasma – a watery substance, and cells which float in the plasma).

Cholesterol is used in the construction of absolutely all the cells in your body, much of it ending up as part of the cell wall. It has been estimated that if there were about a quarter less cholesterol in say a red blood cell (which carries oxygen around the body), then the cell wall which holds it together would disintegrate.

The production of hormones in the body depends entirely on cholesterol. Cholesterol is a vital ingredient of all steroid hormones – adrenalin, oestrogen, testosterone, noradrenaline etc. and without adequate cholesterol these would simply not be produced, with disastrous results. Cholesterol is also an important element in the digestive function.

So reducing cholesterol more than a reasonable amount is undesirable and is one of the main reasons for the negative, sometimes dangerous, effects of drugs which are prescribed to reduce cholesterol artificially. There are in fact two types of cholesterol, and we need to understand these as well as the fatty substances with which they are associated in the body, the lipoproteins.

HDLs and LDLs – Understanding 'Good' and 'Bad' Cholesterol

Amongst the substances which make up the 'total' cholesterol in the body are two different types, which we need to examine. These are high density lipoproteins (HDLs) which are 'good' cholesterols, low density lipoproteins (LDLs) which are 'bad' cholesterols and very low density lipoproteins (VLDLs) which are also harmful. To remember the 'types' try to remember 'low (LDL) is bad' and 'high (HDL) is good'.

Cholesterol is a very complicated subject, so before *Your Control Cholesterol Cookbook* is accused of being too simplistic, let us be absolutely clear: **When speaking of 'good' and 'bad' cholesterol, the terms are relative.** That is to say that we could not actually survive without a reasonable amount of 'bad' cholesterol, so when the term 'bad' is used, it is meant to indicate that when there is too much of it, in relation to the amount of 'good' cholesterol, danger exists.

So the really important issue is not just how much cholesterol there is in your bloodstream, but how much of the 'good' and how much of the 'bad'.

When there are high levels of LDLs there is a big increase in the chance of plaque deposits developing in the arteries, leading to atherosclerosis and perhaps to coronary heart disease.

As we will see, what we eat very much decides whether we have too much (bad) LDL in relation to how much (good) HDL we have, and this is one of the key reasons for care over food selection. LDLs are used in the body to transport cholesterol to particular cells which need them, such as the smooth muscles around blood vessels, the skin and the lymph cells.

High density lipoproteins, on the other hand, carry cholesterol to the liver where it is metabolized and excreted by way of the gall bladder, as bile. So even the 'bad' cholesterol is doing a good job – but only if there is not too much of it. While a great deal of our cholesterol is self-manufactured (mainly in the liver itself), the levels of LDL we carry ('bad' cholesterol) is mainly acquired from what we eat.

LDL – Which Foods?

Major sources of LDL in the diet are found in meat and dairy foods – but surprisingly, as we will see, a high sugar diet also causes increases in LDL. Because excess amounts of LDL is not usable by the body, it tends to get dumped, and unfortunately the dumping ground may just happen to be your arteries. HDL on the other hand helps to 'cleanse' the arteries of LDL cholesterol, but just how this happens is not clear. What we do know for sure is that if we aim for a diet which encourages plenty of HDL, and relatively little LDL, our chances of heart disease, stroke and many other serious ailments decrease. So what are 'safe' levels of cholesterol?

Making Sense of Your Cholesterol Levels

The current official views are that anything above a level of 200 milligrammes of total cholesterol (combined HDL and LDL) per decilitre of blood is dangerous. This is written in shorthand as 'mg/dl' which means 'milligrams per decilitre'. Levels between 200mg/dl and 240mg/dl of total cholesterol are thought to suggest a tendency towards heart disease. Levels above 240mg/dl are considered to indicate a very high risk.

Normal healthy levels of HDL (that's the good cholesterol) in adults in the USA is thought to be 45 to 50mg/dl for men and 50 to 60mg/dl for women. If HDL levels are higher – say above 70mg/dl – the protective effect against heart and circulation disease increases.

It is therefore important when trying to understand test results to pay attention to both the figure for the total cholesterol level and to the levels of HDL and LDL. For example, if you were told your level was 220mg/dl, this would be of concern. It would be less worrying if your HDL count was over 80mg/dl, as this would indicate that your protective HDLs were in good supply.

On the other hand, it is also quite possible to have a relatively low cholesterol reading, say in the region of 150mg/dl, which would normally be considered a 'safe' level. However, if there was an imbalance, say with low levels of HDL of around 50mg/dl at the same time as having relatively high levels of LDL, this would be of concern – even though the total levels of cholesterol were not excessive. It is important therefore to pay attention to the boosting of HDL cholesterol and the reduction of LDL, rather than just thinking of 'cholesterol'. The recipes which have been carefully devised by Alkmini do just that.

The Diet Connection with HDL and LDL

It really is important that we examine what we eat and what we do, and how that can increase total cholesterol, as well as what influences the levels of good HDLs and bad LDLs – so that we can safely keep these substances and situations under control. We also need to understand what we can do to reduce LDL levels if they are already high. Fortunately, a vast amount of research has shown which foods encourage overall cholesterol increase, as well as which increase HDL and reduce LDL.

The recipes in this book are especially aimed at avoiding and reducing LDLs. There will be hardly any foods listed which encourage LDL levels, and most of the recipes actively encourage removal of LDL from the body.

What Influences Your Cholesterol Levels?

Before looking at a number of factors which influence cholesterol levels, and which will help you to understand why some foods are included and some excluded from the recipes in this book, it would be useful to spend just a little time examining the links between sugar, fat and cholesterol levels in the blood.

The Sugar (Refined Carbohydrate) – and the Fat Connection

Research which shows that a high sugar diet leads to increased cholesterol levels was first published in Britain over 25 years ago, when Professor John Yudkin pioneered this approach. More recently in the US, enormous interest has been created by Dr Barry Sears in books such as *The Zone – A Dietary Road Map* (HarperCollins New York, 1995) which have become bestsellers in promoting a diet which is very similar to that indicated by the research evidence quoted in this chapter. When you eat a carbohydrate (a starchy food) which is not used by your body as a source of energy (your body turns carbohydrate into glycogen – the fuel it burns to produce energy), the unused glycogen is stored. Storage capacity is limited, with some going to your muscles and a small amount (enough to meet the body's energy needs for a half a day or so) is held in the liver. What happens to the rest – to the bread, pasta, buns, sweets, juices? Any carbohydrates eaten or drunk, over and above what can be stored as glycogen, is turned by the body into fat and deposited in the layers of the body where this is stored. This tendency to store carbohydrate as fat is even greater when the diet contains an abundance of simple sugars because the pancreas is triggered to produce more insulin, the main controlling substance which the body uses to deal with high sugar intake. Insulin removes excess sugar from the bloodstream and encourages its storage – as fat.

What has this to do with Cholesterol?

The liver is the main area of the body where cholesterol is manufactured. A particular enzyme (a minute but vital chemical substance used in body processes) called HMG CoA reductase, is what decides the rate at which cholesterol is manufactured. When excessive amounts of insulin are being produced by the pancreas, in order to control excessive sugar levels in the blood, one of the by-products of this process is a stimulation of HMG CoA reductase – which means that more cholesterol will be produced – more than is actually needed.

High Sugar Levels – what Causes them ?

A high carbohydrate diet, especially one which includes simple sugars, will boost the levels of your blood sugar. But so will anything which causes the adrenal glands to pump out adrenalin – which is the way the body prepares for action when stressed.

The production of adrenalin leads to sugar being released from the storage depots in the liver and muscles. This prepares the body to defend itself against danger. But when the adrenal glands are repetitively stimulated by stress to produce adrenalin (and therefore sugar) and if as a result blood sugar levels are repetitively raised causing the body to repetitively protect itself (by producing insulin), and as a result even more HMG CoA reductase is produced (which stimulates cholesterol production) we can begin to see how stress can cause an aggravation of a high cholesterol condition! If stimulants such as coffee, alcohol and cigarettes are regularly used – these also stimulate adrenalin and sugar production, and therefore HMG CoA reductase, and therefore cholesterol...

A low sugar, low stress, low stimulant pattern can help to avoid this.

The Fat-Cholesterol Connection

The fats in our diet – especially those derived from animal sources such as meat and dairy foods – are largely LDLs and undesirable.

The total amount of fat we consume adds to the cholesterol load in a direct way – the more fat you eat the more LDLs there will be in the bloodstream. A high fat diet is linked in numerous research studies to atherosclerosis, venous thrombosis, strokes, heart attacks. Saturated fats (solid at room temperature, such as butter and margarine) are twice as powerful in raising serum cholesterol levels (and LDL levels) as are polyunsaturated fats (sunflower and safflower oils for example).

Free Radicals

One of the main factors which makes excessive levels of fat in the blood stream and tissues of the body dangerous is the behaviour of substances called free radicals. These are the substances which cause a sliced apple to go brown, a piece of rubber to perish, metal to rust, your skin to wrinkle with age, your eyes to water when smoke gets in them, your hair to bleach if hydrogen peroxide is put on it (hydrogen peroxide is full of free radical oxidizing agents) and oils to become rancid.

When a sliced apple has lemon juice squeezed over it the browning effect is delayed or stopped. Why? Because lemon juice contains vitamin C, a powerful antioxidant.

Many processed foods which contain oils will have vitamin E added to them. Why? Because vitamin E is a powerful antioxidant and delays rancidity

When you get smoke in your eyes your body produces tears which soothe the irritation. Why? Because tears contain glutathione peroxidase (which contains selenium), a powerful antioxidant which switches off the irritation caused by the free radical activity in the smoke. The processes of rusting, rancidity, ageing and so on are all examples of oxidation.

And just as oils and fats can go rancid in a bottle, so they can in your body, if there are not enough antioxidants in your system to 'quench' the free radical activity which leads to oxidation. Excessive levels of fat combined with inadequate levels of antioxidants, lead to a greater chance of free radical damage, one of the primary causes of arterial damage according to modern research.

How can You Protect Yourself?

By ensuring lower fat levels (hence lower sugar levels) and high levels of antioxidants, either from the diet (fruits and vegetables are the best sources) or from 'health insurance' supplements of antioxidants such as vitamins A, C, E and selenium.

Summary of what Affects Cholesterol Levels

Evidence exists for the following factors having profound influences on overall cholesterol levels, as well as on LDL/HDL ratios. Some of these factors will be examined in more detail later in this chapter.

- Studies have shown that a diet which contains moderately high refined sugar intake for just two weeks led to a number of highly undesirable changes, including:
  - Increased overall cholesterol production.
  - A significant reduction in levels of 'good' HDL cholesterol.
  - An increase in the adhesiveness ('stickiness') of the blood.
  - These changes were shown to be reversible within a few days of dropping sugary foods from the diet and eating according to the principles which this book outlines.[1,2,3]
- Animal fats (meat, poultry, dairy) are our main direct source of LDLs and so these should be severely reduced. Salt, heated fats, margarines, artificial creams, tea, and all refined carbohydrates (white flour etc.) are likely to encourage higher cholesterol levels.[4,5]

- Coconut and palm oil products should be avoided as these will have been processed and heated, changing their molecular structure, and so made undesirable for the body; the same is true for heated fats – such as margarines, which are highly undesirable and should be avoided.[6]
- Drinking coffee regularly and heavily (three or more cups a day) increases cholesterol levels and for this and many other reasons should be stopped or controlled. Numerous researchers, evaluating the coffee drinking habits of thousands of people, taking into account additional habits such as their dietary intake of fats, smoking habits as well as age, sex and weight, have found that there is a direct link between the amount of coffee consumed and the levels of cholesterol (especially LDL cholesterol) in the blood. Three or more cups daily cause the most harm – one or two cups daily seem to make little difference. No similar connection was found with decaffeinated coffee or with tea or cola drinks.[7,8]
- A debate continues as far as eggs are concerned. Firstly, when eggs were eaten regularly by those already on a low-fat diet (such as vegans) the levels of LDL increased. However, when eggs were eaten by people already on a moderate to high-fat diet, there was little influence on the cholesterol levels.[9] When one egg daily was added to the diet of 44 people, 37 of them showed no increase at all in their plasma cholesterol levels.[10] It is suggested that a modest egg intake will do no harm at all on a cholesterol-control diet, say three to four a week, hence there are a few recipes which use eggs in this book.

Other Factors – Drugs and Stress Influence Cholesterol Levels

- Drugs such as the contraceptive pill, steroid medication, many diuretics (Lasix) and the Parkinson's disease drug L-dopa, all increase cholesterol levels.
- Drugs which lower cholesterol have been shown to produce a wide range of serious side effects and this approach is unlikely to produce a healthier person – for one thing the levels of HDL are just as likely to be reduced as are LDLs. This will be discussed later in more detail (*see page 24*).
- When cholesterol in the body is exposed to chemicals such as pesticide residues, chlorine and fluoride (found in most tap water) it can oxidize into an oxysterol, a dangerous form of cholesterol.[11]
- Emotional stress also causes overall cholesterol levels to rise, and helps generate oxysterols. We need to be aware of some of the best methods for stress reduction which can be beneficial in reducing high cholesterol levels (*see page 19*).

Beneficial Influences

- Eating foods which contain water-soluble fibres, such as beans and grains (especially barley and oats, as well as brown rice, lentils, chickpeas (garbanzos), fruits and vegetables) help to reduce high cholesterol levels.[12,13]
- Fish oils are said to encourage more normal levels of cholesterol but this viewpoint remains controversial. Fish should be eaten regularly (two to three times a week) by non-vegetarians, but not excessively. There are some excellent, Mediterranean-inspired fish recipes in this book to encourage regular consumption![14]

- Pure (virgin, cold-pressed) olive oil helps reduce high levels of cholesterol as well as increasing levels of the good cholesterol, HDL. Olive oil is one of the main ingredients of many of Alkmini's recipes and of course is a major feature of the diet in healthy-heart regions of the Mediterranean.[15,16]

- Garlic and onion consumption reduces cholesterol levels and protects the heart and arteries from damage, as well as reducing platelet adhesiveness (stickiness) which can lead to thrombosis. Garlic and onions feature heavily in the Mediterranean diet.[17,18]

- Aubergine (eggplant) also protects against arterial damage because of its 'anti-cholesterol' influence – see the recipes for some amazing aubergine dishes![19]

- Ginger – that versatile and delicious plant – reduces cholesterol as well as preventing excessive adhesiveness of platelets and Alkmini has ensured that a number of recipes feature ginger as a main ingredient.[20]

- Beans contain special water soluble fibres which can help the body to eliminate excessive cholesterol as well as being highly nutritious. These too feature in the recipes for both reasons.[21]

- Pectin, found in apples and pears, has a marked cholesterol lowering effect. Eating just three apples or pears a day, for as little as four weeks, produced significant benefits in medical trials.[22]

- Walnuts, yogurt and alfalfa also protect against cholesterol damage and have been used in many of the recipes in this book. (Research shows that alfalfa protects against cholesterol damage, although the reasons why are not yet clear.)

Why Yogurt?

Yogurt may affect the friendly bacteria which inhabit our intestines and which play a major part in processing bile and cholesterol in the bowels. When the friendly bacteria are healthy they perform these tasks as part of their normal activities. If they are not working well, because of excessive antibiotic use or because of a high sugar, high fat diet, they cannot perform their recycling and detoxification duties efficiently. Since yogurt is a natural food for these bacteria (called lactobacilli because they need lactose which is plentifully found in yogurt) the benefits found regarding cholesterol levels when yogurt (particularly low-fat and 'live') is regularly consumed may relate to improvement in friendly bacteria activity.[23,24]

- We still need to consume oils and fats to maintain good health, but these should be derived from safe sources such as nuts, seeds, grains, pulses (soya beans, lentils etc) and other suitable cold-pressed origins, providing us with monounsaturated oil such as olive oil or polyunsaturated oils such as sunflower or safflower.
- Specific benefits are derived from the lecithin contained in soya beans. Significantly in the Far East, where heart disease is low, soya protein (tofu) takes the place of dairy foods such as cheese. In one study it was found that just 500ml a day of a soya drink reduced harmful fats and cholesterol levels in the blood. Soya products are widely available as 'yogurts' and milk substitute drinks as well as tofu, textured vegetable proteins ('artificial meat') and of course as the beans themselves.[25]
- Eating plent of fresh vegetables and whole grains has a

major contribution in reducing excessive cholesterol levels and should form a major part of the diet, whether raw or cooked. In a controlled study, it was found that regular eating of vegetable leaves and stalks (such as celery) caused a decrease in overall cholesterol levels as well as the dangerous VLDL forms. Eating whole grains (brown flour products) reduced the levels of LDLs.[26]

- Where many of these dietary aids to better heart-health have been combined, the results have been outstanding. When a high complex carbohydrate (whole grains, rice, beans, vegetables), low fat, low cholesterol diet was used, a 50 per cent drop in serum levels of harmful fats and a 21 per cent drop in previously high cholesterol levels was demonstrated, in as little as a month in some cases.[27,28,29,30,31]

- Dean Ornish of the University of California, San Francisco, has shown that a basically vegetarian diet, combined with exercise and stress-reduction methods, reverses the build-up of plaque in the arteries.

The Stress-Cholesterol Connection

- High stress levels lead to...
- High adrenalin stimulation which causes...
- High blood sugar release which leads to...
- HMG CoA reductase which of course increases cholesterol production by the liver, sending up the levels of total cholesterol in the blood.
- When people are under stress there is a tendency for increased free radical activity, which can result in cholesterol being oxidized and turned into oxysterols, which

contribute to plaque formation.

- When stressed there is also a greater tendency for blood cells to clot as they become more adhesive (sticky), adding to plaque levels.

The solution, at least in part, is to reduce stress levels, utilizing relaxation and meditation methods and adequate exercise – all of which have been shown to reduce the risk of cardiac disease.

Suggested Dietary Rules

Desirable and Helpful

- Fibre (from vegetables/grains/fruits – especially apples and similar fruits as well as grapefruit etc.) for its antioxidant nutrient content and the special fibres.
- Soya (for its) lecithin, which reduces cholesterol levels.
- Cold water (oily) fish (for its omega–3 fatty acids) which reduces levels of LDL cholesterol.
- Mediterranean type food (olive oil, fruit, vegetables, garlic, fish) for many reasons including the exceptional heart-health and low cholesterol levels of people following such a diet.
- Monounsaturated oils (olive) and polyunsaturated oils (sunflower, safflower) which are far safer than saturated (hard), mainly animal, fats.
- Vegetarian or fish vegetarian pattern of eating for reasons explained above.

- Eggs in moderation (half their content is monounsaturated) like olive oil, but in excess, especially if overall fat intake is low, can result in increased LDL levels.[32]
- Beans (of any sort) baked, dried and fresh, for their fibre and nutrients.
- Oats (with their bran) are the best grain for lowering cholesterol.
- Yogurt which lowers high cholesterol levels and helps the friendly bacteria.
- Hard (high in calcium etc.) water (rather than soft water) because it helps the heart.
- Particular fruits/vegetables/herbs which have shown heart-health benefits, such as:
  - artichokes
  - alfalfa
  - turmeric -herb
  - aubergine (eggplant)
  - fenugreek
  - rice oil (gamma oryzanol)
  - garlic
  - onion
  - ginger
  - walnuts

Undesirable and Potentially Harmful

- Animal fats – full fat dairy foods such as milk, cream, butter, meat etc.
- Saturated fats – margarine etc.
- Coffee (three or more cups a day).

- Alcohol (up to two drinks daily is harmless. Red wine is possibly helpful).
- Refined sugar.
- Refined carbohydrates (white flour products, polished rice etc.).
- Fried food.
- Smoked food.
- Soft water.

Supplementation

Many nutrients help in reducing cholesterol levels. Those suggested below represent the best methods. Care with diet alone can produce excellent results in reducing cholesterol levels and in promoting HDL and reducing LDL levels. Supplementation, however, is another aspect of nutrition and if the idea appeals to you, the supplements suggested below are safe.

Chromium

Regression of atherosclerotic plaques has been demonstrated with supplementation of chromium, the deposits on the artery walls slowly vanish in many instances. In an experimental double blind crossover study, significant benefits in terms of markers such as total cholesterol (reduced by 7 per cent) and LDL cholesterol levels (reduced by 10 per cent) were observed after six weeks supplementation with chromium tripicolinate (available from most health stores). 200mg daily is suggested.[33] Chromium also helps to maintain stable blood sugar levels.

Nicotinic Acid

Supplementation of nicotinic acid (vitamin B_3) – up to 3g daily – seems to enhance the benefit of chromium supplementation and has been shown to reduce LDL levels significantly. Taking nicotinic acid can produce a flushing sensation which some people find unpleasant.[34]

Vitamin B_6

Vitamin B_6 is helpful because it prevents an undesirable chemical, homocysteine, which is a product of a diet high in animal fats, from causing oxidation damage to cholesterol. 100mg daily is suggested.

Omega–3 Fatty Acids

Taking 3g daily of these special fish oils as a capsule supplement can replace the eating of cold water fish. Supplementation produces reduction in: serum triglycerides, fibrinogen, blood viscosity, red blood cell rigidity, total cholesterol, LDL cholesterol, systolic blood pressure.[35]

If fish oils are taken then Vitamin E should also be supplemented, to prevent peroxidation (when oil goes rancid).[36]
OR

Omega–6 Fatty Acids

Evening primrose oil (and/or borage oil which many people find superior to Evening primrose) may be just as effective in lowering LDL and VLDL cholesterol plasma concentrations and is suitable for vegetarians who do not wish to ingest fish oil (3g daily).[37]

Antioxidant Vitamins

Vitamin E

Supplementation may reduce oxidation of low-density lipo-proteins and is inversely correlated to the risk of mortality from ischemic heart disease.[38] That means the higher the levels of vitamin E in the body, the lower the risk of a heart attack. 600iu suggested daily intake.

Vitamin C

Taking between half a gram and a gram daily (500mg to 1000mg) of vitamin C offers your body extra protection against free radical oxidation damage.

Beta Carotene

Beta carotene is the substance which your body turns into another powerful antioxidant, Vitamin A. Eating enough red and orange vegetables and fruits will give you plenty of beta carotene, but a small supplement of 10,000iu (about 6 milligrammes) offers extra insurance.

An all-purpose antioxidant formulation which contains all of these plus selenium is recommended for simplicity, and these are available at all health food stores and many pharmacies.

Remember that if you eat fresh vegetables and fruits you will provide yourself with most of these nutrients, just as eating fresh fish and free range (organic) poultry (without the fatty skin) will not only give you the protein your body needs but will provide nutrients such as zinc and magnesium as well as important B vitamins. Seeds such as sunflower and pumpkin, and walnuts will offer you rich supplies of zinc and essential

fatty acid (as will cold water fish). A supplement is just that –
it should not replace good eating but can be taken to ensure
that, just in case your diet is missing anything vital, you are
offering it a back-up source.

Other Nutrients

Magnesium, selenium, Coenzyme Q10 and potassium are not
directly connected to cholesterol but are helpful for both pre-
vention and treatment of coronary heart disease.

What About Drugs which Reduce Cholesterol?

A variety of drugs are now used to lower cholesterol, despite
poor overall results in terms of increasing life expectancy.
These drugs are commonly prescribed for people with very
high cholesterol levels. In one famous medical study (The
Helsinki Heart Study) which was completed in 1987, over
4,000 people were treated using either a drug or a dummy
(placebo). The results were impressive. Overall cholesterol
levels in those taking the medication reduced by up to 10 per
cent and the number of heart attacks dropped from the number expected by about one third. This was very impressive.
Unfortunately, although deaths form heart attacks dropped
dramatically, deaths from all other causes went up, so that
more people on the medication died than amongst the group
taking the dummy medicine. Later research has looked at
other drugs and results have been equally equivocal – reduction in cholesterol, reduction in heart attacks, but very little
difference in overall death rates amongst those taking the
drugs. Those people who form a small percentage of the

population who have a genetic predisposition to high cholesterol levels, may well benefit from the use of these drugs. For the majority of people with moderate levels of high cholesterol this may not be the best solution.

Answer?

The answer to most people's high cholesterol levels is:

- To reduce the amount of cholesterol consumed in the diet, although this is not the most important part of the programme.
- At the same time, the diet being followed should reduce the amount of self-manufactured cholesterol – and this calls for care over selection of carbohydrates in general and sugars in particular.
- Particular attention should be given to reducing LDLs and raising HDL levels.
- At the same time the diet should be providing a good level of all the essential nutrients – including adequate protein and fat – needed for good health.
- Stress reduction tactics should form another basic requirement for dealing with excess cholesterol and enhancing health.
- Suitable exercise is vital – whether this is in the form of aerobic or anaerobic exercise is up to your particular condition, and your likes and dislikes. What is essential for good health is that you regularly do something to get the circulation going, to stimulate your metabolism to burn excess fatty deposits and to achieve the proven benefits of regular physical activity – whether this is through sport,

walking, swimming or exercise classes. But the focus of this book is your dietary habits and how you can easily, pleasurably and safely help yourself to maintain normal levels or to reduce excess levels of cholesterol...

It is with these guidelines in mind – a low cholesterol intake, reduced cholesterol production, balancing the 'good' and 'bad' cholesterols at the same time as offering a good nutritional balance – that Alkmini has put together the delicious and nutritious recipes in this book.

Notes

1. Sears, B. *The Zone*, Regan Books, New York, 1995.
2. Yudkin, J. *et al.* 'Effects of Dietary Sugar', *British Medical Journal* 281:1396, 1980.
3. Yudkin, J., Szanto, S. 'Relationship between Sucrose Intake, Plasma Insulin and Platelet'.
4. Weisweiller, P. *et al.* 'Influence of Polyunsaturated Fat Restriction on Serum Lipoproteins in Humans', *Metabolism* 34(1):83–87, 1985.
5. Hagsted, D. 'Serum-cholesterol Response to Dietary Cholesterol', *American Journal of Clinical Nutrition* 44(2):299–305, 1986.
6. Kummerow, F. 'Nutrition Imbalance and Angiotoxins as Dietary Risk Factors in Coronary Heart Disease', *American Journal of Clinical Nutrition* 32:58–83, 1979.
7. Mathias, S. *et al.* 'Coffee, Plasma Cholesterol and Lipoproteins: A Population Study in an Adult Community' *American Journal of Epidemiology* 121(6):896–905, 1985.
8. Kark, J. *et al.* 'Coffee, Tea and Plasma Cholesterol', *British Medical Journal* 291(6497):699–704, 1985.

9. Dawber, E. *et al.* 'Eggs, Serum Cholesterol and Coronary Heart Disease', *American Journal of Clinical Nutrition* 36:617–625, 1982.

10. Bronsgeest-Schoute *et al. American Journal of Clinical Nutrition* 32:2193–2197, 1979.

11. Morin, R. 'Role of Cholesterol Oxidation in Pathogenesis of Atherosclerosis', *Annals of Clinical and Laboratory Science* 19(4):225–237, 1989.

12. Hillman, L. *et al.* 'The Effects of the Fiber Components of Pectin, Cellulose and Lignin on Serum Cholesterol Levels', *American Journal of Clinical Nutrition* 42(2):207–213, 1985.

13. Jenkins, D. *et al.* 'Effect of Pectin, Guar Gum and Wheat Fiber on Serum Cholesterol', *Lancet* pp1116–1117, May 17 1975.

14. Kromhout, D. *et al.* 'Inverse Relation between Fish Consumption and 20-Year Mortality from Coronary Heart Disease', *New England Journal of Medicine* 312:1205–1209, 1985.

15. Mensink, R. *et al.* 'Effect of Monounsaturated Fatty Acids Versus ComplexCarbohydrates on High Density Lipoproteins in Healthy Men and Women', *Lancet* 1:122–125, 1987.

16. Keys, A. *et al.* 'Lowering Plasma Cholesterol by Diet', *New England Journal of Medicine* 314:745–748, 1986.

17. Ernst, E. 'Garlic and Blood Lipids', *British Medical Journal* 291:139, 1985.

18. Bordia, A. 'Effect of Garlic on Blood Lipids in Patients with Coronary Heart Disease', *American Journal of Clinical Nutrition* 34:2100–2103, 1981.

19. Mitschek, G. *Expermntelle Pathologie,* Vol.10, 1975.

20. Backon, J. 'Ginger : Inhibition of Thromboxane Synthetase and Stimulation of Prostacycline: Relevance for Medicine and Psychiatry', *Med. Hypotheses* 20:271, 1986.

21. Anderson, W. 'Effects of Legumes (Beans) and their Soluble Fiber on Cholesterol-rich Lipoproteins', *American Jnl Soc. Abstracts* AGFD No. 39, 1982.

22. Sable-Amplis, R. *et al.* 'Further Studies on Cholesterol Lowering Effect of Apple Pectin in Humans', *Nutritional Research* 3:325–328, 1983.

23. Hepner, B. *et al.* 'Hypocholesterolemic Effect of Yogurt', *American Journal of Clinical Nutrition*, 32:19–24, 1979.

24. Alfalfa, M. *American Journal of Clinical Nutrition* 1810–1812, 1979.

25. Check, W. 'Switch to Soy Protein for Boring but Healthful Diet', *Journal American Medical Association* 247:345–346, 1982.

26. Fraser, G. 'The Effect of Various Vegetable Supplements on Serum Cholesterol', *American Journal of Clinical Nutrition* 34:1272–1277, 1981.

27. Rosenthal, M. *et al.* 'Effects of a High-Complex-Carbohydrate Low Fat Low Cholesterol Diet on Serum Lipids and Estradiol', *American Journal of Medicine* 78:23–27, 1985.

28. Kushi, L. *et al.* 'Diet and 20-year Mortality from Coronary Heart Disease', *New England Journal of Medicine* 312(13):811–818, 1985.

29. Reiser, S. *et al.* 'Blood Lipids, Lipoproteins, Apo-proteins and Uric Acid in Men Fed Diets Containing Fructose or High Amylose Cornstarch', *American Journal of Clinical Nutrition* 49:832–839, 1989.

30. Winitz, M. *et al.* 'Effects of Dietary Carbohydrate on Serum Cholesterol Levels', *Archives Biochem. Biophys.* 108:576–579, 1964.

31. Forde, O. *et al.* 'The Tromso Heart Study: Coffee Consumption and Serum Lipid Concentrations in Men with Hypercholes-terolaemia – A Randomised Intervention Study', *British Medical Journal* 290:893–895, 1985.

32. Sacks, E. *et al.* 'Ingestion of Egg Raises Plasma Low Density-Lipoproteins in Free Living Subjects', *Lancet* 2:647–649, 1984.

33. Press, R. *et al.* 'Effects of Chromium Picolinate on Serum Cholesterol and Apoliprotein B Fractions in Human Subjects', *West J Med.* 152:41–45, 1990.

34. Urberg, M. *et al.* 'Hypercholesterolemic Effect of Nicotinic Acid and Chromium Supplementation', *Journal of Family Pract.* 27(6):603–606, 1988.

35. Kinsella, J. *et al.* 'Dietary n–3 Polyunsaturated Fatty Acids and Amelioration of Cardiovascular Disease, *American Journal of Clinical Nutrition* 52:1–28, 1990.

36. Laganiere, S. *et al.* 'High Peroxidizability of Subcellular Membrane Induced by High Fish Oil Diet is Reversed by Vitamin E', *Clinical Research* 35:A565, 1987.

37. Chan, J. *et al.* 'Dietary A-Linolenic Acid is as Effective as Oleic Acid and Linoleic Acid in Lowering Blood Cholesterol in Normolipidemic Men', *American Journal of Clinical Nutrition* 53:1230–1234, 1991.

38. Gey, K. *et al.* 'Inverse Correlation between Plasma, Vitamin E and Mortality from Ischemic Heart Disease in Cross Cultural Epidemiology', *American Journal of Clinical Nutrition* 53:326SS–334S, 1991.

Special Notes and Preparation Tips

Be Careful but not Fanatical

Diet plays a large part in cholesterol production – you should try to avoid those foods which provoke the body into producing too much cholesterol – especially sugar-rich and refined carbohydrate foods. Remember that stress also encourages cholesterol production so that obsessive attention to every detail of the 'do's and don'ts' in this book, while helping reduce cholesterol on one level, could be encouraging it on another, if you are feeling pressured and stressed by the whole enterprise. In other words, use common sense in the application of the guidelines we have presented. The occasional lapse in relation to any of the undesirable foods will almost certainly not make you ill or your symptoms worse. The regular pattern of eating and how you live your life are the factors which are important, not the odd deviation from the diet – but please don't take that as a license to not try at all. There are a few foods which although undesirable in excessive amounts (see notes below about eggs for example) do appear amongst the recipes in small quantities. We considered not including any of these foods at all in the recipes (it would have been quite easy to avoid them altogether) and eventually decided that by including a few, in small amounts, we could signal to you that you should allow yourself some slack, without feeling guilty.

Dairy Foods and Fats

Foods which should, in the main, be avoided are those which contain animal fats, e.g. all meat, the skin of poultry and any fat-rich dairy foods as well as all refined carbohydrates (the reasons are explained in Chapter 2). Hence there are only a few dairy foods in the recipes and these are always urged to be 'virtually fat-free'. In contrast, fish oils and fresh oils from seeds and nuts, especially olive oil and flaxseed oil, are included and desirable. Nuts such as walnuts have been shown to offer particularly beneficial effects in high cholesterol individuals, when consumed regularly and in high quantities.

Oils

It will not take you long when looking through the recipes which follow to note that olive oil is frequently recommended. There are many reasons for this which space does not allow us to explain, however the brief résumé is that this monounsaturated oil has major health enhancing properties. As an alternative, safflower oil is also recommended. Any recipes which call for olive oil may be substituted with safflower oil if you wish, although it is not as beneficial. The olive oil suggested should always be first pressing, cold-pressed, virgin if at all possible. Never use butter or a butter substitute. When used for cooking a less expensive olive oil will do instead of virgin first (cold) pressed versions which can be expensive.

Eggs

Some well known experts suggest that eggs are a factor in promoting cholesterol increase – since they contain the substance, and this has become part of popular mythology, 'Don't eat eggs or your cholesterol levels will go up'. The truth is that research has shown that when individuals, with or without high cholesterol levels, are placed on a high egg diet (several daily) the levels of cholesterol, as measured over a number of weeks, do not change significantly – unless the eggs are prepared in specific ways.

It seems that fried eggs, and hard boiled eggs, because of the heat they are subjected to in the cooking process, can produce slightly increased cholesterol levels, whereas scrambled, poached or soft-boiled eggs do not have this effect. The recipes in this book in the main avoid eggs in any quantity because of the belief many people have about them – not because they can in fact do much to aggravate a cholesterol problem. Therefore, where eggs do appear in the recipes the recommendation is often to use the whites only which would reduce altogether the chance of cholesterol increase. Be reassured though that eggs are not a problem – if you cook them correctly.

Salt – Yes or No?

Many of the recipes which follow contain the suggestion 'sea salt to taste'. There have been concerns about excess sodium (part of salt) in conditions such as high blood pressure. If this is a factor, and if a low salt diet has been suggested then you should be aware that salt substitutes exist. The best of these is potassium chloride (salt is sodium chloride), available from most health stores as well as pharmacies. In the UK 'Ruthmol' is recommended as a salt substitute.

Vegetarian – Yes or No?

A lot of the savoury dishes are vegetarian (no meat or fish) and some are vegan (no animal products at all) as these patterns of eating, following extensive trials, are known to help people with cholesterol – as discussed in earlier chapters (and as proven by research by experts such as Dr Dean Ornish – to reduce cholesterol levels most efficiently). You don't need to become vegetarian but try to incorporate vegetarian dishes into your regular pattern of eating. Vegetarian (and vegan) foods are delicious, easy to prepare and will ease you towards eating patterns most likely to reduce cholesterol levels and help cardiovascular illness.

Tofu

One of the best 'animal protein alternatives' is the soya bean product, tofu. This bland 'soy-cheese' has little taste in itself but takes on the flavours of foods with which it is cooked, hence its common presence in the recipes of the vegetarian dishes described in this book. The inclusion of tofu is almost always described as optional in the recipes, but is highly recommended.

Garlic

This wonderful herb/vegetable is much in evidence in the recipes in this book and a word is needed regarding both its sometimes pungent aroma and the many benefits which it offers. Its proven health benefits include it being an antiseptic, antifungal and antiparasitic agent which helps to heal an unhealthy digestive system; it lowers high blood pressure, reduces cholesterol levels very efficiently; reduces adhesiveness of the blood (very important in cardiovascular disease); helps reduce catarrhal congestion, improves absorption of some of the B-vitamins and is useful in controlling high sugar levels in diabetes.

As to the smell. We cannot deny that it has a pungent odour when raw but this virtually vanishes when cooked (however so do some of its benefits) and almost all the uses suggested in this book are for cooked garlic, so the smell should not be an issue. If this ever does present a problem then chewing a few sprigs of raw parsley after your meal will sweeten the breath. Different types of garlic are available, those with white and those with pink skins, with the white ones being 'stronger' both in flavour and odour. When buying garlic, test the heads for freshness by pressing them to assess their firmness. If on pressure there is a spongy feel, the head of garlic is old and drying out. So seek firm ones.

Quantities

You can expect a head of garlic to yield between 12 and 14 cloves, and not unnaturally the larger the head the larger the cloves. These are easier to peel than small ones (the paper-like skin must be removed before use). A large crushed or chopped clove will produce approximately 1 to 1¹/₂ teaspoons of garlic.

Spring Garlic

Spring garlic is easy to grow and is delicious. Just break up a head of garlic and press the individual cloves into the soil, 5 cm/2 inches or so apart, into window box or pot, or in the garden, and within weeks you will have delicate spring-onion-like shoots. When they are 12 to 15 cm (5 to 6 inches) tall, harvest them by pulling them out of the ground. After trimming off the root use these chopped (bulb, stem, leaves and all) on a salad or cooked with vegetables (artichoke for example) or in soup for a rare and delicate flavour experience.

Serving Cooked Vegetables

Whether steamed, lightly boiled or stir-fried, individual vegetables such as fennel, cauliflower, courgettes (zucchini), spring greens and wild vegetables (see below) can have their flavour enhanced markedly by using a few simple tactics.

1) As an alternative to serving them hot, straight from the cooking process, consider serving vegetables at room temperature as they do in Southern Europe. After being cooked in whichever is the most convenient way (steaming retains most of the nutrient value as does stir-frying) the vegetables should be placed on a serving dish and allowed to cool to room temperature.

2) Just before being served (hot or cold), dress with olive oil (virgin, first cold pressing) and lemon juice. The flavour of vegetables served in this way is superior, especially when served at room temperature.

3) A few cloves of garlic cut into paper thin slices and scattered on vegetables such as greens, makes a dramatic additional flavour.

Wild Vegetables

The nutritional value as well as the amazing flavours of wild vegetables remain a mystery to most people. Try exploring the possibility of adding comfrey, nettle tops (just the tender young leaves or shoots), dandelion or mustard greens to your diet.

Incidentally, cultivated dandelion greens are available at many continental and ethnic (Greek, Italian, Spanish, Arab/Middle Eastern etc.) food shops which are now so widespread. Try harvesting greens from sites free of traffic pollution if possible, and away from sites regularly visited by dogs – for obvious reasons. Choose young tender leaves as the older ones can be fibrous and hard to chew. The greens should be well washed, and either steamed or boiled for about 15 minutes until tender. Drain and serve with lemon juice and olive oil dressing. They are amazingly rich in nutrients and will do wonders for the bowels.

Beans

Some of the recipes place emphasis on soaking dried beans overnight, cooking for a while and then changing water and other particular instructions. If followed these suggestions will ensure that the enzymes which produce flatulence are removed, so making sure that there is no bloating, a common bean after-effect! It is preferable to use dried beans, but as a speedy alternative, you may use tinned varieties. Simply drain and rinse, then re-heat for a few minutes.

Ginger

Ginger features in a number of the recipes because of its proven anti-cholesterol influences as well as its benefits to digestion and health in general. This can be purchased as a purée (widely available) and in its uncooked form as root ginger. If it is going to be used in a grated form it helps to deep freeze the root first, it then grates much more easily and loses nothing in flavour, aroma or nutritional value. We urge you to use it abundantly.

Preparing Globe Artichokes

Immediately before using artichokes in any of the recipes in this book the following procedures should be followed to ensure that the vegetable is ready for use and that its inedible parts have been removed.

1) Cut away the stem close to the head and remove most of the leaves until the tender ones are reached.
2) Cut the artichoke into two halves, cutting it from the top to the bottom.
3) With a grapefruit knife, remove the choke, which is the hairy covering of the heart of the vegetable.
4) Squeeze the juice of half a lemon into a saucepan together with a 850 ml (30 fl oz/3³/₄ cups) of cold water.
5) With the other half of the lemon rub the newly exposed surfaces of the artichoke before placing it in the lemon water (this prevents browning – oxidation – of the exposed surfaces).
6) The tender leaves and the peeled stem (after rubbing with lemon juice) may also be placed in the saucepan and used in subsequent recipes.
7) Remove the artichoke, or its parts, from the lemon water immediately prior to use in recipes.

Preparing Rice

The only rice used in this book is the vitamin (B_1, B_2, B_6) and mineral (magnesium, potassium, iron) rich unpolished (brown) varieties – and not the devitalized and almost nutrient-free polished (white) versions, which provide empty calories and little else. Different varieties of rice have quite varied requirements in their cooking, however in general the following guidelines are valid.

1) If you are using a pressure cooker, which is recommended, then follow the manufacturer's instructions.

2) For regular cooking, rinse the rice in tepid water and place in a saucepan with a lid (cast iron is best for cooking rice, if you are not using a pressure cooker). Add water, ensuring that there is approximately 4 cm ($1\frac{1}{2}$ inches) of water above the surface of the rice. In dry climates more water and in humid climates less water may be needed than is suggested below. Remember that the more water used, the softer the rice will be after cooking. A reasonable guide to quantities would be – for 420 g (14 oz/2 cups) of rinsed and drained brown rice use 1,200 ml (40 fl oz/5 cups) of water for cooking. This quantity would serve 4 people.

3) Once the water containing the rice is boiling, reduce the heat until it is gently simmering, then cover, ensuring that the lid of the pot fits tightly.

4) Do not stir the rice during the cooking as this may cause it to become 'sticky'.

5) Approximately 45 to 55 minutes is required to cook whole rice but this may vary depending on the hardness of the water being used.

6) If during the cooking additional water is required (if the rice is clearly not cooked and the water has virtually all evaporated for example) already boiling water should be added very carefully so that the process is not disturbed. Since rice absorbs water as it cooks, and different varieties absorb more or less water, an accurate recommendation as to the quantity of water required is not possible.

7) When cooked, toss the rice gently using a wooden spoon or spatula and allow it to stand in a bowl (wooden is best) for several minutes before serving.

Brown Rice and Sesame Seeds

In order to produce a rice and sesame seed combination, follow the above method for rice, but add dry roasted sesame seeds to the rice at the beginning of the cooking process. The seeds are prepared as a follows:

1) For the quantity of rice described in the Preparing Rice instructions (420 g/14 oz/2 cups of unpolished brown rice), a quantity of 90 g (3 oz/^{1}/₂ cup) of unhulled sesame seeds is suggested.
2) Wash and drain the sesame seeds and place in a skillet/pan and dry roast over a medium heat, stirring constantly.
3) When the seeds begin to turn brown, remove from the heat and allow to cool.
4) Sprinkle the seeds onto the rice before the cooking process begins and cook following normal rice instructions.
5) This variation on plain rice is delicious. Alternatively, add the dry roasted seeds to the rice after it is cooked, just before serving.

Breakfast

Hot, High Fibre Millet, Oats and Nut Breakfast

Serves 1

This high fibre, quickly cooked, millet-based breakfast provides an ideal start to the day with powerful cholesterol lowering influences.

Metric (Imperial)		American
3 tbsp	millet, washed	3 tbsp
480 ml (16 fl oz)	water	2 cups
pinch	salt substitute	pinch
1 piece of fruit	peach, apricot, apple or pear (peeled, diced)	1 piece of fruit
1 tbsp	raisins	1 tbsp
2 tbsp	rolled oats	2 tbsp
1$^1/_2$ tbsp	chopped walnuts or almonds (optional)	1$^1/_2$ tbsp
$^1/_2$ tsp	cinnamon (optional)	$^1/_2$ tsp

1) Place the millet plus half the water and the pinch of salt substitute into a saucepan. Cover, bring to the boil and simmer for 15 minutes.
2) Add the remaining water, fruit and oats. Bring the contents to the boil and then simmer for a further 10 minutes, covered, stirring regularly. Uncover and cook for a final 2 minutes.
3) Serve, optionally topped with chopped nuts and a sprinkling of cinnamon.

Pomegranate, Wheat and Nuts

This dish is eaten cold and if it is to be used as a breakfast meal it should be completely prepared the night before as the wheat requires cooking for almost an hour.

Serves 2

Metric (Imperial)		American
300 g (10 oz)	wheat	1$\frac{1}{2}$ cups
2	pomegranates	2
40 g (1$\frac{1}{2}$oz)	raisins or sultanas	$\frac{1}{3}$ cup
85 g (3 oz)	walnut halves	1 cup
2 tbsp	natural, live fat-free yogurt	2 tbsp

1) Wash the wheat and place in a saucepan. Cover with cold water. Allow to stand overnight.
2) Drain and replace with fresh water to cover the wheat. Bring to the boil and simmer until tender (40 minutes to an hour).
3) Skin and remove the seeds from the pomegranates.
4) Drain wheat and place in a serving bowl and add all the other ingredients.

Cook's Note

This recipe is also delicious served as a dessert.

Seed and Nut Power Breakfast

This recipe is based on the principles of Stone Age eating, in which grains are avoided and the foods which would have been easily available to our hunter-gatherer ancestors are used because they are energy rich and nourishing – providing minerals, vitamins and essential fatty acids – as well as fibre. Use a coffee mill or food processor to grind the nuts. You can store surplus quantities in the fridge for a few days. If you don't have time to grind the nuts, use them whole. Ideal for a controlled-cholesterol diet.

Serves 1

Metric (Imperial)		American
1 tbsp	sunflower seeds	1 tbsp
1 tbsp	pumpkin seeds	1 tbsp
$^1/_2$ tbsp	linseeds	$^1/_2$ tbsp
$^1/_2$ tbsp	sesame seeds	$^1/_2$ tbsp
30 g (1 oz)	freshly ground almonds or walnuts or pecans	$^1/_3$ cup
30 g (1 oz)	dried apricots or peaches, chopped and unsulphured	$^1/_4$ cup
1	dessert apple or diced pear, grated	1
$^1/_2$ or 1	mango or papaya, peeled and diced	$^1/_2$ or 1
1 tbsp	flaxseed oil* (optional)	1 tbsp

1) Place the seeds into a bowl and barely cover with water. Soak overnight.
2) Just before breakfast add the ground nuts, dried fruit, fresh fruit and flaxseed oil (optional).
3) Chew well.

* Flaxseed oil provides essential fatty acids, and is available from good health food stores. It should be kept refrigerated.

Cook's Note

If you wish, add the dried fruit to the seed mixture before soaking overnight. Add the fresh fruit, milled nuts and oil (optional) in the morning. Alternatively, add a tablespoon or two of flaked wheat, millet or oats to the seed mixture before it is soaking overnight (if there is no sensitivity to grains).

Swiss 5-Grain Breakfast

Warning: This recipe should be avoided if you are wheat or grain sensitive.

Based on a traditional Swiss recipe, this breakfast is used in many health spas throughout Europe and provides enormous energy, plenty of fibre – cholesterol lowering influences – and has great nutritional value.

Serves 1

Metric (Imperial)		American
1 tbsp each of	whole wheat, rye, oats, barley or millet, freshly milled	1 tbsp each of
2 tbsp	oat bran	2 tbsp
2 tbsp	raisins or Hunza apricots, unsulphured and depipped	2 tbsp
340 ml (12 fl oz)	water	1¹/₂ cups
1 tbsp	flaxseed oil* (optional)	1 tbsp

Slow (Overnight) Method

1) The evening before use, coarsely grind the grains, using a coffee grinder.
2) Place all of the ingredients into a saucepan with the water.
3) Bring to the boil and simmer for 7 to 10 minutes.

4) Remove from the heat and wrap the saucepan in a blanket or newspapers and allow to stand overnight.
5) If the resulting porridge is too loose, use less water next time.
6) Reheat and serve with flaxseed oil (optional) together with freshly made or bought unsweetened apple or pear purée or stewed (no sugar) pears or apples.

Alternative (Rapid) Method

1) Place all of the ingredients into a saucepan and cover with boiling water.
2) Allow to stand for half an hour (time for the cereals to absorb the liquid) before serving as above, with flaxseed oil (optional), apples or pears (puréed or stewed without sugar).
3) This second (uncooked) version retains more nutritional value but requires a lot more chewing and is not recommended for people with irritable bowels.

* Flaxseed oil provides essential fatty acids, and is available from better health food stores. It should be kept refrigerated.

No-Yolk Ginger Omelette

This recipe is adapted from that of Dr Dong and his co-author Jane Banks who wrote the book *New Hope for Arthritics* some 20 years ago. Dr Dong was strictly against the use of all dairy foods, meat and egg yolks in his diet, and very pro-fish. His 'eggless' omelette makes a useful variation for breakfast since it is nutritious and tasty and yet avoids egg yolks, which many people with cholesterol problems choose to avoid.

Serves 1

Metric (Imperial)		American
1 tbsp	olive or safflower oil	1 tbsp
15 g ($^1/_2$oz)	ginger, finely grated	$^1/_8$ cup
2	egg whites, unbeaten	2
	salt substitute to taste	

1) Using a non-stick frying pan and the small amount of oil suggested, slightly sauté the ginger for approximately 30 seconds to soften it, then remove from the pan and place into a bowl which contains the unbeaten egg whites.
2) Gently stir the ginger into the egg whites until a good mixture is achieved and then add a touch of salt substitute.
3) Place this mixture into the still heated frying pan and cook until it is just browning before turning it and cooking the other side in the same way. Serve immediately.

Cook's Note

This dish is ideal as a snack and can be served any time of day.

Oatmilk and Oat Porridge Plus

All the benefits of oatmeal are preserved in this oatmilk-oatmeal combination. Wheatgerm (which is rich in vitamin E) and tahini are available at all health stores and many supermarkets. Walnuts are also useful in a cholesterol-controlled diet.

Serves 1

Metric (Imperial)		American
425 ml (15 fl oz)	oat (or soya or rice) milk	2 cups
	milk	2 cups
pinch	sea salt	pinch
100 g (3oz)	porridge oats	³/₄ cup
1 tbsp	tahini (sesame paste) or honey (optional)	1 tbsp
1 tbsp	wheatgerm (optional)	1 tbsp
1 tbsp	walnuts, crushed (optional)	1 tbsp

1) Place the oat (or other plant source) milk and a pinch of salt into a saucepan and heat slowly. Bring to the boil.
2) Reduce heat and gradually add the oats, stirring constantly.
3) Keep stirring until the porridge reaches thick (but not solid) consistency (or the consistency you like) – up to 10 minutes.
4) Serve having added the tahini and/or wheatgerm and/or crushed walnuts.

Yolk-Free Omelette

Serves 1

Metric (Imperial)		American
1 tbsp	olive or safflower oil	1 tbsp
30 g (1 oz)	mushrooms, sliced	$^1/_4$ cup
1	medium tomato, sliced	1
1	spring onion (scallion), sliced (optional)	1
2	egg whites, unbeaten	2
	salt to taste	
4 twists	black pepper	4 twists

1) Heat the oil in a non-stick frying pan. When hot, add the mushrooms, tomato and spring onion (scallion) (optional) and sauté until just softened. Remove from the pan and place into a bowl with the unbeaten egg whites.
2) Gently stir the vegetables into the egg whites until a good mixture is achieved and then add a touch of salt and pepper to taste.
3) Place this mixture into the still heated frying pan and cook until it is just browning. Turn and cook the other side in the same way.
4) Serve.

Dips

Aubergine (Eggplant) Dip

This traditional Greek dish with its high fibre content is an excellent food for anyone watching their cholesterol intake. It can be used as a starter or with soup as a side dish or as a party dip together with Hummus (*see page 55*) or Walnut and Garlic Dip (*see page 61*).

Serves 4–6

Metric (Imperial)		American
2	large aubergines (eggplants)	2
370 ml (13 fl oz)	virgin olive oil	2 cups
225 ml (8 fl oz)	soya milk	1 cup
225 ml (8 fl oz)	lemon juice	1 cup
60 g (2 oz)	tofu, crumbled	$^1/_2$ cup
	salt substitute to taste	
5 twists	black pepper	5 twists

1) Wash and dry the aubergines (eggplants) and cook in the oven at 180°C/350°F/Gas Mark 4 for 1 to 1¹/₂ hours. When cooked, remove the contents and discard skins.
2) Place the flesh in a mixing bowl and reduce to a creamy texture.
3) Work this with a pestle and mortar, adding alternately the oil, soya milk and lemon juice. Alternatively, use a food processor.
4) When it achieves a 'frothy' texture add the crumbled tofu.
5) Season with salt substitute and pepper.
6) Place into a bowl and garnish with slices of tomato, parsley and black olives.
7) Refrigerate before serving as a main meal with wholemeal toast (for a complete protein combination – tofu and soya milk both derive from a pulse and toast from a grain so that together these provide all the amino acids needed for complete protein) with a mixed salad or it can be offered as a starter with celery or carrot sticks.

Hummus

This traditional Turkish/Middle Eastern dish can be served as a
starter or with soup as a side dish or as a party dip together
with the Aubergine (Eggplant) Dip (*see page 53*) or Walnut
and Garlic Dip (*see page 61*) .

Serves 4–6

Metric (Imperial)		American
280 g (10 oz)	dried chickpeas (garbanzos)	1^1/$_2$ cups
	or	
420 g (14 oz)	tinned chickpeas (garbanzos)	2^1/$_2$ cups
2 sprigs	fresh rosemary	2 sprigs
210 ml (7^1/$_2$ fl oz)	lemon juice	1 cup
290 ml (10 oz)	virgin olive oil (plus extra)	1^1/$_3$ cups
	salt substitute to taste	
5 twists	black pepper	5 twists
3 tbsp	tahini, ready made*	3 tbsp
8 (or more)	garlic cloves, crushed	8 (or more)

1) Wash the chickpeas (garbanzos) and then soak in water
   overnight, ensuring that the water covers them completely.

2) In the morning the chickpeas (garbanzos) will have swollen to double their size. Discard the water, rinse them well and place them with fresh water into a saucepan, to cover by at least 2¹/₂ cm/1 inch and slowly bring to the boil.

3) White froth will appear and this should be removed, and the water allowed to boil.

4) Add the rosemary and simmer until the beans are tender. This can vary from 30 to 90 minutes depending upon the quality of the water and the chickpeas (garbanzos).

5) When the chickpeas (garbanzos) are tender add a quarter of the lemon juice, half the olive oil, salt substitute and the pepper and continue simmering.

6) When the chickpeas (garbanzos) are really soft they are ready for the next stage which is to remove them from the saucepan and place them into a food processor. Retain at least 210 ml (7¹/₂ fl oz/1 cup) of the cooking liquid.

7) Add this liquid and the remaining ingredients to the processor and blend these together at a low speed. Taste and add more seasoning if necessary.

8) Place the resulting mixture into a bowl, cover this with a thin layer of olive oil to prevent it drying out and refrigerate.

9) Initially the mixture may appear somewhat runny. This will vary with the quality of the chickpeas (garbanzos) used and is somewhat unpredictable. The hummus will thicken as it cools.

10) Serve as a main meal with wholemeal toast (for a complete protein combination) alongside a mixed salad or it can be offered as a starter with celery or carrot sticks.

* Tahini is a sesame seed paste obtainable at good grocers or health stores.

Cook's Note

If using tinned chickpeas (garbanzos), simply drain and rinse, then re-heat for a few minutes (with the rosemary), then follow the recipe from stage 5.

Garlic Potato – Corfu Style

This dish is one of the greatest delights of Greek cooking – simple, powerfully flavoursome and highly nutritious. It can be served as a relish, enhancing almost any savoury or vegetable meal, or can be used as a dip (with celery sticks, carrots, radishes, cucumber).

Serves 4–6

Metric (Imperial)		American
1.8 kg (3¹/₂ lb)	potatoes	13 cups
2	large heads of garlic (about 20 cloves), peeled and crushed	2
	sea salt to taste	
370 ml (13 fl oz)	olive oil	1¹/₂ cups
4	lemons (juiced)	4
3 slices	lemon	3 slices
6	black olives	6
2 sprigs	parsley	2 sprigs

1) Boil the unpeeled potatoes in salted water.
2) Crush the garlic into an empty mixing bowl.
3) Peel the cooked potatoes and add these to the bowl while still hot.
4) Add a pinch of salt and use a mixer to reduce the potato and garlic mix to a pulp.

5) Now, bit by bit, alternately blend the olive oil and lemon juice into the potato/garlic mixture, blending constantly, either using a pestle and mortar (which can be very tiring but gives the best results) or using a food processor. If the mixture is not creamy when all ingredients have been blended in (probably because of potato quality which can vary in the degree of starch they contain) add a little (a tablespoon or two) water and a little additional lemon juice to the mixture and process some more (this should take about 20 minutes altogether). Place the creamy mixture into a serving bowl and garnish with lemon slices, olives and parsley.
6) This dish has a very strong garlic flavour so use more or less garlic according to taste.
7) Serve hot with savoury meals or cold with any cooked vegetables (for example, Mixed Vegetable Salad on page 65).

Cook's Note

To give the dish a green look, and to reduce its garlic odour, add and thoroughly mix in to the mixture 115 g (4 oz/4 cups) of finely chopped parsley just before it has been completely blended.

Olive Dip

This dip may be served as a relish for savoury dishes or with celery, cucumber and/or carrot sticks and/or warm brown toast as an appetizer or dip.

Serves 4–6

Metric (Imperial)		American
455 g (1 lb)	black olives (depipped)	3 cups
90 ml (3 fl oz)	olive oil	$^1/_3$ cup
6	garlic cloves, crushed	6
60 ml (2 fl oz)	lemon juice	$^1/_4$ cup
1 tbsp	oregano	1 tbsp
3 twists	black pepper	3 twists
	lemon slices to garnish	

1) Using a food processor, blend the depipped olives until they reach a creamy consistency.
2) Add the remaining ingredients and mix thoroughly.
3) Place in a bowl and garnish with lemon slices.
4) Serve.

Walnut and Garlic Dip

This attractive dip is an ideal relish which can be eaten with a savoury meal or a salad using carrot, cucumber, celery sticks or radishes.

Serves 4–6

Metric (Imperial)		American
5	garlic cloves, peeled and crushed	5
55 g (2oz)	wholemeal bread, soaked in water and squeezed to damp state	1 cup
	salt substitute to taste	
285 ml (10 fl oz)	olive or vegetable oil	1^1/$_3$ cups
85 g (3 oz)	ground walnuts or almonds	1 cup
90 ml (3 fl oz)	cider vinegar	^{1}/$_3$ cup

1) Place crushed garlic in a mixing bowl with the moist breadcrumbs.
2) Add salt substitute to taste and mix well.
3) Into another bowl gradually add together the soaked bread, oil, ground nuts and cider vinegar, blending these all the while.
4) If the mixture becomes too thick (it should have a paste-like texture) add a little warm water.

Salads

Mixed Alfalfa and Ginger Salad

Serves 1 as side dish

Metric (Imperial)		American
1	medium tomato, skinned and diced	1
85 g (3 oz)	bean sprouts	1 cup
85 g (3 oz)	alfalfa sprouts	1 cup
15 g ($^1/_2$ oz)	fresh basil leaves	$^1/_2$ cup
1 tsp	fresh ginger, grated	1 tsp
$1^1/_2$ tbsp	olive oil	$1^1/_2$ tbsp
1 tbsp	lemon juice or cider vinegar	1 tbsp
4 twists	black pepper	4 twists
	sea salt to taste	

1) Wash all of the vegetables thoroughly, place into a colander and drain.
2) Place into a serving bowl, add the remaining ingredients and toss gently.

Cook's Note

Walnuts or almond flakes may be added if desired.

Avocado, Cabbage and Cauliflower Salad

Serves 2

Metric (Imperial)		American
115 g (4 oz)	cabbage, finely shredded	2 cups
115 g (4 oz)	cauliflower florets, chopped	2 cups
30 g (1 oz)	parsley, chopped	$^{1}/_{2}$ cup
60 g (2 oz)	onion, finely chopped	$^{1}/_{2}$ cup
170 g (6 oz)	avocado, diced	1 cup
2 tbsp	lemon juice	2 tbsp

1) Place the cabbage and cauliflower into a bowl together with the parsley and chopped onion.
2) Separately dice the avocado and cover with the lemon juice (this prevents the avocado turning brown).
3) Combine the avocado with the other ingredients and serve with a dressing of your choice (*see pages 169–171*) and, if desired, the sliced banana.

Cook's Note

Sliced banana tastes wonderful with this salad and one or two of these could be sliced up and added to the salad just before serving, if desired.

Cooked Mixed Vegetable Salad

For anyone with a delicate digestion who finds salads a problem, a cooked salad makes an interesting variation. You can use frozen peas if you don't have fresh ones.

Serves 1

Metric (Imperial)		American
1	carrot, well washed and sliced	1
110 g (4 oz)	French beans,	1$\frac{1}{4}$ cups
$\frac{1}{2}$	trimmed fennel bulb, cut into large pieces	$\frac{1}{2}$
1	globe artichoke, quartered (see page 38)	1
1	large potato cut into cubes	1
115 g (4 oz)	peas	$\frac{3}{4}$ cup
1	celery stick, strings removed and sliced	1
2	small courgettes (zucchini), sliced	2
1	small beetroot, cooked and diced	1
10	black olives	10
1	small Spanish onion, sliced	1

Dressing

2 tbsp	olive oil	2 tbsp
1 tbsp	cider vinegar	1 tbsp
$^1/_2$ tsp	oregano	$^1/_2$ tsp
	salt to taste	

1) Place the carrot, beans, fennel, artichoke, potato cubes and peas into a steamer and steam for 10 minutes.
2) Add the celery and courgette (zucchini) slices and steam for a further 5 minutes.
3) Empty onto a serving dish and add the diced beetroot, the olives and the raw onion.
4) Mix together the dressing ingredients, pour over the vegetables and serve.

Cook's Note

This cooked salad tastes just as good, perhaps better, if eaten at room temperature (as it often is in the Mediterranean) and dressed with lemon juice

Fennel and Butter (Lima) Bean Salad

The combination of butter (lima) beans with herbs and other ingredients make this salad a nutritional treasure house of particular value to anyone on a full or semi-vegetarian diet.

Serves 2 to 3 as side dish

Metric (Imperial)		American
200 g (7 oz)	dried butter (lima) beans	1 cup
	or	
420 g (14 oz)	tinned butter (lima) beans	$2^1/_2$ cups
120 g (4 oz)	onions, diced	1 cup
1 tsp	oregano	1 tsp
120 g (4 oz)	fennel, finely diced	1 cup
120 ml (4 fl oz)	olive or vegetable oil	$^1/_2$ cup
1 tbsp	cider vinegar	1 tbsp
4 twists	black pepper	4 twists
	sea salt to taste	
8	large black olives, depipped	8

1) After washing, soak the butter (lima) beans overnight in water.
2) Rinse thoroughly and add fresh cold water.
3) Bring to the boil and simmer for 20 minutes.

4) At the same time, bring a kettle of water to the boil.
5) Discard the cooking water and replace with fresh boiling water and a little salt (to taste) and cook until tender.
6) Remove from heat and empty beans into a salad bowl.
7) Add the remaining ingredients, apart from the depipped olives.
8) Toss gently and add olives before serving. Serve either warm or after cooling to room temperature.

Cook's Note

If using tinned butter (lima) beans, simply drain and rinse, then follow the recipe from stage 5.

Chickpea (Garbanzo) and Ginger Salad

The chickpeas (garbanzos) are high in fibre, making this salad highly nutritious, easy to digest and delicious.

Serves 2

Metric (Imperial)		American
300 g (10 oz)	dried chickpeas (garbanzos) or	$1^1/_2$ cups
420 g (14 oz)	tinned chickpeas (garbanzos)	$2^1/_2$ cups
240 ml (8 fl oz)	olive oil	1 cup
115 g (4 oz)	onion, grated	1 cup
2 tsp	dried rosemary	2 tsp
75 g (3 oz)	root ginger, freshly grated	$^1/_2$ cup
4 twists	black pepper	4 twists
	salt substitute to taste	

1) Wash the chickpeas (garbanzos) and soak in water overnight, ensuring that the water covers them completely.
2) Discard the water and rinse thoroughly, removing any froth which has formed.

3) Place the chickpeas (garbanzo) in a saucepan, cover with fresh water and bring to the boil.
4) At the same time, bring a kettle of water to the boil.
5) Simmer for 10 minutes, remove from heat and discard the cooking water, replacing with fresh boiling water from the kettle.
6) Add all other ingredients and simmer until tender, or when all water has evaporated, stirring from time to time.
7) Serve at room temperature as a salad, or hot as a side dish.

Cook's Note

If using tinned chickpeas (garbanzos), simply drain and rinse, then follow the recipe from stage 4.

Butter (Lima) Bean Salad

Serves 4 to 6 as side salad

Metric (Imperial)		American
455 g (1 lb)	dried butter (lima) beans	2^1/$_2$ cups
	or	
840 g (1 lb 12 oz)	tinned butter (lima) beans	5 cups
1 level tbsp	sea salt	1 level tbsp
280 ml (10 fl oz)	olive oil	1^1/$_3$ cups
2 tbsp	lemon juice or cider vinegar	2 tbsp
2	spring onions (scallions), chopped	2
30 g (1 oz)	flat-leaf parsley, chopped	1 cup
1	medium onion, chopped	1
2	celery stalks, chopped	2
5 twists	black pepper	5 twists

1) Soak the butter (lima) beans overnight, drain and wash well.
2) Place in a saucepan, cover with water and bring to the boil.

3) As soon as boiling starts, froth forms. Remove this and continue to boil at a moderate heat for 30 minutes.
4) Add the salt and cook until tender – times will vary depending upon bean characteristics (30 to 120 minutes).
5) Drain the beans and return to the saucepan.
6) Add the olive oil, lemon juice or cider vinegar and pepper and mix gently but well.
7) Leave to cool for 20 minutes and then add the remaining ingredients, and gently mix.
8) Place in a bowl and serve.

Cook's Note

If using tinned butter (lima) beans, simply drain and rinse, then re-heat for a few minutes, then follow the recipe from stage 6.

Lentil Summer Salad

Serves 2 as salad

Metric (Imperial)		American
200 g (7 oz)	small brown lentils	1 cup
1	medium onion, chopped	1
2	spring onions (scallions), chopped	2
4 tbsp	olive oil	4 tbsp
1 tbsp	cider vinegar	1 tbsp
2	garlic cloves, crushed	2
$^1/_4$ tsp	mustard powder	$^1/_4$ tsp
$^1/_2$ tsp	dried oregano	$^1/_2$ tsp
6 twists	black pepper	6 twists
	sea salt to taste	
30 g (1 oz)	fresh parsley	$^1/_2$ cup

1) Place the lentils in a saucepan and cover with water.
2) Add the salt and simmer until tender (approximately 30 to 50 minutes).
3) Remove from heat and drain.
4) Separately, mix all of the ingredients except the lentils and parsley. Add to the lentils while they are still warm.
5) Refrigerate for at least 1 hour.
6) Just before serving add the parsley.

Lettuce and Orange Salad

Serves 2 as a side dish

Metric (Imperial)		American
1	cos (romaine) lettuce	1
1	large navel orange	1
2 tbsp	olive oil	2 tbsp
pinch	cayenne pepper	pinch
pinch	paprika	pinch
pinch	sea salt	pinch
3 tbsp	walnuts	3 tbsp

1) Clean and chop the lettuce.
2) Peel the orange, leaving as much pith as possible. Slice into discs and then quarter them.
3) Combine the lettuce, orange, oil, seasoning and nuts.
4) Toss gently and serve.
5) Ideally served alongside any poultry dish.

Root Salad and Walnuts

Serve this salad with the Vinaigrette Dressing on page 171.

Serves 2

Metric (Imperial)		American
1	medium beetroot	1
1	large carrot	1
1	small celeriac	1
1	horse radish	1
$^1/_4$	cucumber	$^1/_4$
2	large radishes	2
6	cherry tomatoes	6
60 g (2 oz)	mustard and cress	1 cup
85 g (3 oz)	walnuts, freshly shelled and halved	1 cup

1) Wash and peel all root vegetables.
2) Using a peeler, make thin ribbons of all the root vegetables.
3) Place these into a bowl together with tomatoes, cress and walnuts and add the vinaigrette. Mix well.
4) Serve together with Tomatoes Provençal (*see page 162*) or on its own.

Walnut and Cabbage

Serves 2 to 3

Metric (Imperial)		American
350 g (12 oz)	cabbage, shredded	6 cups
1	avocado, diced	1
1	carrot, grated	1
2	spring onions (scallions), chopped	2
1 tbsp	fresh ginger, grated	1 tbsp
250 g (8oz)	walnuts, hand chopped	2 cups

Dressing

2	garlic cloves, crushed (optional)	2
140 ml (5 fl oz)	olive oil	$^2/_3$ cup
90 ml (3 fl oz)	lemon juice	$^1/_3$ cup
8 twists	black pepper	8 twists
	sea salt to taste	

1) Place all salad ingredients into a bowl.
2) Mix the dressing ingredients in a small bowl and add to the salad.

3) Accompanied with wholemeal bread, olives and fat free cheese, this makes an excellent, light, nourishing meal. The Vinaigrette (*see page 171*) is a good alternative dressing.

Turkey Salad

Serves 2 as a main course

Metric (Imperial)		American
455 g (1 lb)	cooked turkey, diced	2 cups
4	radishes, diced	4
1	medium onion, diced	1
2	celery stalks, chopped	2
$^1/_2$	green (bell) pepper, sliced	$^1/_2$
$^1/_2$	red (bell) pepper, sliced	$^1/_2$
30 g (1 oz)	flat-leaf parsley, chopped	$^1/_2$ cup
3 tbsp	walnuts	3 tbsp
3 tbsp	almond flakes	3 tbsp

Dressing

4 tbsp	olive oil	4 tbsp
$1^1/_2$ tbsp	lemon juice	$1^1/_2$ tbsp
1 tsp	curry powder	1 tsp
6 twists	black pepper	6 twists
$^1/_2$ tsp	brown sugar	$^1/_2$ tsp
	sea salt to taste	

1) Place all the vegetable ingredients into a salad bowl.
2) Mix the dressing ingredients in a cup or small bowl and add to the salad bowl.
3) Mix gently but thoroughly.
4) Just before serving, line the plates with lettuce leaves.

Soups

Chicken and Rice Soup

Serves 3 to 4

Metric (Imperial)		American
1 leg, 1 breast	chicken, skinned	1 leg, 1 breast
2	carrots, diced	2
1	medium potato, diced	1
1	medium onion, chopped	1
2	celery sticks, diced	2
2	medium, ripe tomatoes, chopped	2
2 tbsp	olive oil	2 tbsp
4 twists	black pepper	4 twists
	sea salt to taste	
225 g (8 oz)	parboiled brown rice	1 cup

1) Wash the chicken well (ensure all visible fat as well as skin has been removed) and place into a saucepan, cover

with ³/₄ litre (1¹/₂ pints/3³/₄ cups) of water and bring to the boil. Cook for 40 minutes.

2) Add all the other ingredients apart from the rice.
3) Cook until the chicken and vegetables are tender (approximately 30 minutes).
4) Remove the chicken and add the rice to the remaining ingredients and continue to simmer.
5) Meanwhile, remove the bones from the chicken and cut into small pieces and add this to simmering soup, stir and cook for a further 5 minutes.
6) Remove from heat and serve – or, for a less solid consistency, place in blender for 30 seconds before serving.

Fish Soup

Rice flakes are available from most healthfood stores and larger supermarkets.

Serves 3 to 4

Metric (Imperial)		American
2	carrots	2
1	medium potato	1
1	medium onion	1
2 stalks (+ leaves)	celery	2 stalks (+ leaves)
3 tbsp	olive oil	3 tbsp
4 twists	black pepper	4 twists
	sea salt to taste	
455 g (1 lb)	white fish, cleaned and descaled (e.g. cod)	2$\frac{1}{2}$ cups
3 tbsp	rice flakes	3 tbsp
3 tbsp	lemon juice	3 tbsp

1) Clean and dice the vegetables and place them into a saucepan with $\frac{3}{4}$ litre (1$\frac{1}{2}$ pints/3$\frac{3}{4}$ cups) of water, olive oil and seasoning.
2) Bring to the boil and cook for 30 minutes on a moderate heat.
3) Add the whole fish and cook for a further 15 minutes, on a moderate heat. Remove from the heat.

4) Using a ladle put the fish onto a large plate and remove the bones (check that no bones remain in the saucepan).
5) Return the fish to the saucepan and bring back to the boil, at which time add the rice flakes and lemon juice.
6) Stir well and boil for a further 1 minute.
7) Remove and allow to cool for 5 minutes, then serve.

Green (French) Bean Soup

Serves 2 to 3

Metric (Imperial)		American
225 g (8 oz)	fresh French beans	2$^{1}/_{2}$ cups
2	large potatoes	2
90 ml (3 fl oz)	olive oil	$^{1}/_{3}$ cup
1	medium onion, chopped	1
1 tbsp	rice flour	1 tbsp
2 tbsp	rice flakes	2 tbsp
1 tsp	cider vinegar	1 tsp
4 twists	black pepper	4 twists
30 g (1 oz)	chives, chopped	$^{2}/_{3}$ cup
	sea salt to taste	
2 tbsp	soya milk, concentrated	2 tbsp

1) Wash and destring beans and chop into small segments.
2) Peel the potatoes and cut into small cubes.
3) Boil the beans and potatoes in 1$^{1}/_{2}$ litres (3 pints/7$^{1}/_{2}$ cups) of water until soft.
4) Strain and save the stock.
5) Heat the olive oil in a saucepan, add the onion and fry on a moderate heat until light brown.
6) Add the rice flour and cook for 1 minute, stirring all the while. Add stock and cook for 2 minutes (until slightly thickened).

7) Add the cooked beans and potatoes and all the other ingredients apart from soya milk.
8) Stir on a gentle heat for a minute.
9) Just before serving, add the soya. Sprinkle with chopped chives.

Potato and Leek Soup

Serves 3

Metric (Imperial)		American
3	medium leeks	3
3	medium potatoes	3
1	large onion	1
140 ml (5 fl oz)	olive oil	$^2/_3$ cup
4 twists	black pepper (optional)	4 twists
	sea salt to taste	
500 ml (16 fl oz)	oatmilk (or soya milk)	2 cups

1) Peel and dice the vegetables into small pieces.
2) In a saucepan, add the vegetables to 240 ml (8 fl oz/1 cup) of water, seasoning and olive oil.
3) Bring to the boil and simmer until vegetables are tender (approximately 30 minutes).
4) Remove from the heat and place the cooked ingredients into a blender, add oatmilk and blend for 1 minute.
5) If consistency is too thin, mix in a spoonful or two of rice flakes or rice flour.
6) Serve with toast and olives.

Lentil and Garlic Soup

Unlike the Thick Lentil and Tomato Soup (*see page 91*) this one is built around the lentils, whereas the other contains lentils but comprises more tomatoes and other vegetables. Both are delicious and highly nutritious, offering a complete high fibre, mineral rich, low fat, high protein meal when eaten with bread (grains and pulses together provide complete protein).

Serves 3 to 4

Metric (Imperial)		American
280 g (10 oz)	small brown lentils	1^1/$_2$ cups
10	garlic cloves, unpeeled and uncrushed	10
2 tbsp	tomato purée (paste)	2 tbsp
1 tbsp	dry oregano	1 tbsp
8 twists	black pepper	8 twists
120 ml (4 fl oz)	olive oil	^{1}/$_2$ cup
	sea salt to taste	

1) Wash lentils and place in saucepan with 850ml (1^1/$_2$ pints/ 4 cups) cold water.
2) Bring to the boil and simmer for 30 minutes.
3) Add all the other ingredients and cloves of garlic.

4) Cook for a further 30 minutes adding extra boiling water if consistency becomes too thick (different types of lentil will absorb more or less water).
5) The soup is ready when the texture is thick but not excessively so.
6) Serve with low-fat cheese.

Mediterranean Peasant Soup

Serves 2

Metric (Imperial)		American
80 g (2$^{1}/_{2}$oz)	celery leaves, chopped	$^{1}/_{2}$ cup
2	medium tomatoes, chopped	2
1	medium onion, chopped	1
1	medium carrot, chopped	1
85 g (2$^{1}/_{2}$oz)	fennel bulb, chopped	$^{1}/_{2}$ cup
80 ml (2$^{1}/_{2}$ fl oz)	olive oil	$^{1}/_{2}$ cup
4 twists	black pepper	4 twists
	sea salt to taste	
150 g (5 oz)	small pieces of brown pasta	1$^{1}/_{2}$ cups

1) Place all the ingredients, except for the pasta, into a saucepan.
2) Add 1 litre (1$^{1}/_{2}$ pints/4 cups) cold water and bring to the boil (partially cover the saucepan).
3) When the vegetables are tender (approximately 45 minutes) add the pasta and stir.
4) Continue cooking for 20 minutes, until the pasta has softened.

5) Remove from heat and serve with wholemeal or rye toast, black olives and fat-free fromage frais to turn this into a nourishing main meal.

Thick Lentil and Tomato Soup

Unlike the Lentil and Garlic Soup (*see page 87*) this one is built around tomatoes and other vegetables plus lentils.

Serves 4

Metric (Imperial)		American
90 ml (3 fl oz)	olive oil	$^1/_3$ cup
1 tsp	paprika	1 tsp
1	medium onion, coarsely chopped	1
3	celery stalks, chopped	3
2	large carrots, peeled and chopped	2
150 g (5$^1/_2$ oz)	fresh tomatoes, blanched, peeled and finely chopped	1 cup
430 ml ($^3/_4$ pint)	boiling water	2 cups
90 g (3 oz)	red split lentils	$^1/_2$ cup
1 tsp	dried thyme	1 tsp
28 g (1 oz)	sun-dried tomatoes	1 tsp
2 tsp	lemon juice	2 tsp
5	garlic cloves, crushed	5
285 ml (10 fl oz)	tomato juice	1$^1/_2$ cups
6 twists	black pepper	6 twists
$^1/_4$ tsp	oregano	$^1/_4$ tsp

1) Into a saucepan place the oil, paprika, chopped onion, celery, carrots and tomatoes.
2) Cook gently for approximately 10 minutes.
3) Add the boiling water, lentils, thyme, sun-dried tomatoes, lemon juice and three quarters of the crushed garlic and cook gently for a further 10 to 15 minutes.
4) Put half a pint of the partially prepared soup into a liquidizer with the tomato juice and process this together with the remaining garlic.
5) Return the liquidized mixture to the saucepan, bring back to boil, stirring well.
6) Season with black pepper and serve with oregano sprinkled on top.

Vegetables with Artichoke

Serves 3

Metric (Imperial)		American
1	medium potato	1
1	medium carrot	1
2	Jerusalem artichokes	2
1	globe artichoke (see page 38)	1
1	medium onion	1
1 tbsp	fresh dill, finely chopped	1 tbsp
60 g (2 oz)	green peas	$^1/_2$ cup
3 tbsp	olive oil	3 tbsp
4 twists	black pepper	4 twists
	sea salt to taste	
2 tbsp	couscous	2 tbsp
2 tbsp	fresh parsley, finely chopped	2 tbsp
	lemon juice	

1) Peel and dice the potato, carrot, artichokes and onion.
2) Place these in a saucepan together with the dill, peas, olive oil and 1$^1/_2$ litres (3 pints/7$^1/_2$ cups) of water.
3) Bring to the boil and simmer for 40 minutes.
4) Add seasoning and cook for a further 15 minutes.
5) Remove from the heat and cool for 15 minutes.

SOUPS

6) Carefully empty three quarters of the contents into a blender and whizz until smooth.
7) Empty back into the saucepan together with the unblended ingredients. Add the couscous. Bring to the boil slowly and simmer for 5 minutes, stirring constantly. Add a little (boiling) water if texture is too thick.
8) Serve sprinkled with parsley (and a few drops of lemon juice per serving, if desired).

Vegetarian Dishes

Mushrooms Stuffed with Almonds

Serves 2

Metric (Imperial)		American
2	large, open mushrooms	2
1	medium tomato, chopped	1
30 g (1 oz)	parsley, chopped	¹/₂ cup
1	spring onion (scallion), chopped	1
4	garlic cloves, chopped	4
2 tbsp	olive oil	2 tbsp
2 tbsp	almond flakes	2 tbsp
2 tbsp	ground almonds	2 tbsp
2 tbsp	brown breadcrumbs	2 tbsp
1	egg white	1
1 tbsp	tomato juice	1 tbsp
8 twists	ground black pepper	8 twists

                    sea salt to taste
2 sprigs   fresh parsley   2 sprigs

1) Wash the mushrooms, then remove the stalks.
2) Chop the stalks and add to the other ingredients (apart from the parsley), mix together.
3) Stuff this mixture into the whole mushrooms.
4) Place these into an oven container (stuffed side up) and bake for 30 minutes at 190°C/375°F/Gas Mark 5.
5) Garnish with fresh parsley and serve with salad or cooked vegetables or rice for a complete meal.

Artichoke Moussaka

Serves 4 to 6

Metric (Imperial)		American
4	artichokes	4
200 g (7 oz)	brown rice	1 cup
4	garlic cloves, chopped	4
30 g (1 oz)	parsley, chopped	$^1/_2$ cup
30 g (1 oz)	dill, chopped	$^1/_2$ cup
3	spring onions (scallions)	3
140 ml (5 fl oz)	olive oil	$^2/_3$ cup
1	large tomato, chopped	1
1 tsp	tomato purée (paste)	1 tsp
5 twists	black pepper	5 twists
	sea salt to taste	
3	large potatoes	3
3 tbsp	pine nuts	3 tbsp
2 tbsp	black raisins	2 tbsp
1 serving	béchamel sauce (see page 163)	1 serving

1) Clean and prepare the artichokes (*see page 38*).
2) Boil the halved artichokes until they are tender (retain a cup of the water for use in béchamel sauce). Drain and leave to cool.

VEGETARIAN DISHES

3) Meanwhile place the rice (*see page 39*) into a saucepan and cook for 10 minutes.

4) Add the garlic, parsley, dill, onions, olive oil, tomato, tomato purée (paste) and seasoning and cook until all of the water has evaporated (approximately 20 to 30 minutes), stirring occasionally.

5) When cooked, remove from the heat.

6) Meanwhile add oil to a suitable oven container (e.g. a lasagne dish).

7) Take the boiled potatoes, skin if not organically grown and cut into thick (1 cm) slices and layer these on the base of the container

8) Slice the cooked artichokes into halves again and scatter 2 or 3 slices onto the potatoes. Season.

9) Add to the cooked rice and herbs the pine nuts and raisins and mix well. Empty onto the layer of artichokes/potatoes and smooth with a spoon.

10) Onto this place a further layer of the remaining potatoes and artichoke quarters, and season.

11) Prepare the béchamel sauce. Pour over the dish and smooth with a spoon.

12) Place into a preheated oven 190°C/375°F/Gas Mark 5 and cook for 45 to 60 minutes until crust is golden brown.

13) Serve hot or cold – usually warm, with salad.

Chickpea (Garbanzo) and Ginger Spheres

Serves 2 to 4

Metric (Imperial)		American
340 g (12 oz)	dried chickpeas (garbanzos)	2 cups
	or	
420 g (14 oz)	tinned chickpeas (garbanzos)	2¹/₂ cups
2 tbsp	fresh rosemary	2 tbsp
	sea salt to taste	
2	egg whites	2
1 tbsp	ginger, freshly grated	1 tbsp
5 twists	ground black pepper	5 twists
1	medium onion, chopped	1
180 ml (6 fl oz)	olive oil	²/₃ cup
455 g (1 lb)	tomatoes, chopped	2 cups

1) Soak the chickpeas (garbanzos) overnight, then discard the water.
2) Place in a saucepan, cover with fresh water and bring to the boil (remove any froth which is produced).
3) Add the rosemary and half a teaspoon of sea salt.
4) Cook until tender (approximately 60 minutes).
5) Remove from heat and drain.

6) Place in a food processor and turn into pulp while still warm.

7) When cool, add the slightly beaten egg whites, ginger and ground pepper.

8) Meanwhile place the onion, oil and tomatoes into a saucepan with seasoning and 280 ml ($^1/_2$ pint/$1^1/_3$ cups) of water and cook for 10 minutes, stirring frequently.

9) Now take a small amount of chickpea (garbanzo) mixture, shape into balls and place into the simmering tomato/onion sauce.

10) If the spheres are not completely covered, add a little boiling water to thin the sauce.

11) Bring to the boil and cook for 10 to 15 minutes or until the water has evaporated.

Cook's Note

If using tinned chickpeas (garbanzos), simply drain and rinse, then re-heat for a few minutes (with the rosemary), then follow the recipe from stage 5.

Ginger Stir-Fried Vegetables and Tofu

Tofu provides the protein and essential nutrients found in soya beans and it absorbs the flavours of the foods with which it is cooked. Stir-frying vegetables ensures that little of their value is lost in the cooking while they are heated sufficiently to become more easily digestible. The ginger content adds to digestibility of this dish.

Serves 2 to 4

Metric (Imperial)		American
30 g (1 oz)	cashew or pistachio nuts, shelled	$^1/_4$ cup
2 tbsp	olive or safflower oil	2 tbsp
2	carrots, sliced	2
1	courgette (zucchini), sliced	1
2	celery sticks, sliced	2
3	spring onions (scallions), chopped	3
120 g (4 oz)	mushrooms, whole or sliced	1 cup
120 g (4 oz)	mangetout	1 cup
120 g (4 oz)	tofu, cubed or sliced	1 cup
1 tbsp	ginger, grated	1 tbsp

1) Place the nuts into either a wok or a deep frying pan and dry roast these for a few minutes until they darken in colour. Stir-fry them to prevent burning. Remove the nuts and place them on a plate to cool.
2) Lightly oil the pan using half the oil and stir-fry the carrots for a minute or two before adding the rest of the vegetables, tofu and the remaining oil.
3) Constantly stir the ingredients as they cook for a further minute or two.
4) Add the grated root ginger and the nuts and cook for a further 30 seconds before turning out the contents into a serving dish.
5) Serve with rice or as an accompaniment to any savoury dish.

Cook's Note

If you enjoy the taste of ginger you might want to add a teaspoon or two of ginger purée to the vegetables when they are placed in the pan to cook.

Globe Artichokes with Herbs

Serves 2 to 4

Metric (Imperial)		American
4	globe artichokes	4
	juice of 1 lemon	
8 small	new potatoes	8 small
60 g (2 oz)	parsley, chopped	1 cup
60 g (2 oz)	dill, chopped	1 cup
4	spring onions (scallions), chopped	4
5	garlic cloves, chopped	5
140 ml (5 fl oz)	olive oil	$^2/_3$ cup
6 twists	black pepper	6 twists
	sea salt to taste	

1) Cut away the artichoke stem close to the head and remove the tougher leaves until the tender ones are exposed.
2) Cut artichokes in half, removing all hairy filaments covering the heart.
3) With the juice of half a lemon wipe all surfaces of the artichoke to prevent discolouration (oxidation) which is rapid.
4) Place into a saucepan and cover with water, with the remaining lemon juice.
5) Add the rest of the ingredients and bring to the boil, and cook gently until all the water has evaporated (approximately 1 hour).

6) Serve on its own with wholegrain bread as a snack or as a side dish with any savoury meal.

Greek-Style Oven Roasted Butter (Lima) Beans

This traditional Greek peasant dish is high in protein and fibre. Serve with green vegetables or almost any of the side dishes in this book, this makes an excellent main course.

Serves 4 to 5

Metric (Imperial)		American
455 g (1 lb)	dried butter (lima) beans	2 cups
	or	
840 g (1 lb 12 oz)	tinned butter (lima) beans	5 cups
455 g (1 lb)	tinned tomatoes	2 cups
6	garlic cloves, halved lengthways	6
2	celery stalks (plus leaves), chopped	2
2	small onions, chopped	2
2	medium carrots, chopped	2
15 g ($^1/_2$oz)	parsley, chopped	$^1/_4$ cup
1 tsp	paprika	1 tsp
120 ml (4 fl oz)	olive oil	$^1/_2$ cup

1) Soak the beans overnight. Rinse then place in boiling water and cook for 30 minutes.

2) Discard the water and replace with fresh boiling water (to remove 'wind' inducing enzymes) and cook for a further 30 minutes.

3) Drain and place the beans in a casserole dish 2 to 3 inches (5 to 6 cm) deep together with the remaining ingredients which have been mixed. Cover with water.

4) Cover with aluminium foil and place in a preheated oven at 180°C/350°F/Gas Mark 4 for 60 minutes.

5) Remove the foil and continue cooking until all of the water has evaporated and the beans are tender (but not soft). Some browning or crispness should be seen on the surface.

6) The timing of cooking these beans varies considerably depending upon their quality and type, as well as the hardness of the water.

Cook's Note

If using tinned chickpeas (garbanzos), simply drain and rinse, then follow the recipe from stage 3. Reduce the cooking time to 5 minutes.

Herb-Stewed Artichokes

There are few more cleansing vegetables than artichokes with their proven beneficial effects on liver function. When combined with parsley, garlic and onions the benefits are amplified. This delicious, wholesome and easily made vegetarian dish is widely eaten in Eastern Europe

Serves 3 to 8

Metric (Imperial)		American
4	artichokes (see page 38)	4
180 g (6 oz)	spring onions (scallions), chopped	1¹/₂ cup
60 g (2 oz)	parsley, chopped	1 cup
455 g (16 oz)	peas, fresh or frozen	3 cups
180 ml (6 fl oz)	olive or vegetable oil	²/₃ cup
	sea salt to taste	
6 twists	black pepper	6 twists

1) Prepare the artichokes (*see page 38*) so that they are dechoked and halved.
2) Place the artichokes, onions, parsley and peas into a large (non-stick if possible) saucepan and add the olive oil, salt and pepper and cover with water. Bring to the boil and simmer until all the water has evaporated. Stir from time to time during the cooking.

3) Serve hot or at room temperature.
4) If this is eaten as a main course, complement it with olives, wholemeal bread and the Walnut and Garlic dip (*see page 61*). As a side dish it is ideal with any of the fish or poultry recipes in this book.

Rice and Mushroom Stew

Serves 2 to 4

Metric (Imperial)		American
300 g (10 oz)	long grain brown rice	1^1/$_2$ cups
230 g (8 oz)	fresh button mushrooms, halved	2 cups
5	garlic cloves, chopped	5
3	spring onions (scallions), chopped	3
180 ml (6 fl oz)	olive oil	^{2}/$_3$ cup
330 ml (10 fl oz)	sieved tomatoes (passata)	1^1/$_2$ cups
30 g (1 oz)	parsley, chopped	^{1}/$_2$ cup
30 g (1 oz)	dill, chopped	^{1}/$_2$ cup
6 twists	black pepper	6 twists
	sea salt to taste	

1) Rinse the rice. Place in a pan with water. Bring to the boil and cook for 20 minutes.
2) Add the remaining ingredients to the rice. Stir well and cook for 20 minutes.
3) If the water has been absorbed and the rice is not tender, add a cupful of boiling water.
4) If this is to be served as a main course, add 2 tablespoons of sunflower seeds, pumpkin seeds and/or broken walnuts just before serving.

Mushrooms and Tofu with Garlic and Ginger

This excellent combination offers unusual flavours and nutritious ingredients.

Serves 2

Metric (Imperial)		American
225 g (8 oz)	button mushrooms	2 cups
30 g (1 oz)	ginger, freshly grated	$^{1}/_{4}$ cup
115 g (4 oz)	onions, grated	1 cup
8	garlic cloves, chopped	8
240 ml (8 fl oz)	olive oil	1 cup
pinch	cayenne pepper	pinch
4 twists	black pepper	4 twists
120 ml (4 fl oz)	water	$^{1}/_{2}$ cup
	sea salt to taste	
225 g (8 oz)	tofu, cubed	1 cup

1) Wash the mushrooms, cut them in half and place in a shallow saucepan.
2) Add the other ingredients apart from the tofu, and heat gently, uncovered, until the contents are sizzling.
3) Cover and simmer gently, stirring from time to time, until all the water has evaporated (about 25 minutes).
4) About 5 minutes before the cooking is finished, when there is still a little liquid in the saucepan, add the tofu cubes and mix well.

5) Served with rice or couscous this dish provides a full protein meal.

Nut and Seed Roast

Serves 4 to 6

Metric (Imperial)		American
1	large onion, chopped	1
6	garlic cloves, cut lengthwise	6
140 g (5 oz)	olive oil	$^2/_3$ cup
5 tbsp	raw cashew nuts	5 tbsp
5 tbsp	walnuts	5 tbsp
5 tbsp	sunflower seeds	5 tbsp
5 tbsp	pumpkin seeds	5 tbsp
5 tbsp	almond flakes	5 tbsp
3 tbsp	pine nuts	3 tbsp
4 slices	wholemeal bread	4 slices
2	large eggs	2
pinch	chilli pepper	pinch
6 twists	black pepper	6 twists
	sea salt to taste	
210 ml (8 fl oz)	sieved tomatoes	$1^1/_2$ cups
2	medium tomatoes	2

1) Place the onion, garlic and olive oil into a large frying pan and sauté until the ingredients are brown. Remove from the heat.

2) Meanwhile, place cashew nuts, walnuts, sunflower and pumpkin seeds into a food processor and grind finely. Place into a bowl and add the almond flakes and pine nuts.

3) Place the bread into the food processor and process until only crumbs are present. Put into a separate bowl.

4) Beat the eggs lightly in a cup.

5) Into the pan (with the onions and garlic) gradually blend in the ingredients from the other containers (mixed seeds and nuts, breadcrumbs, beaten egg as well as the sieved tomatoes) with a wooden spoon.

6) When all the ingredients have been blended (apart from the whole tomatoes) you should be left with a thick, damp consistency.

7) Prepare a bread tin by lining it with foil and brush with olive oil. Into this pour in the mixture and pat to even out.

8) Cut tomatoes into thick slices and cover the surface. Season and bake in a preheated oven at 200°C/400°F/Gas Mark 6 and cook for 60 to 80 minutes.

9) Serve hot or cold, with salad or fresh vegetables.

Stuffed Aubergine (Eggplant)

Serves 4

Metric (Imperial)		American
4	medium size, round aubergines (eggplants)	4
200 g (7 oz)	brown rice	1 cup
30 g (1 oz)	parsley, chopped	¹/₂ cup
2	medium tomatoes, chopped	2
2	spring onions (scallions), chopped	2
1	medium onion, chooped	1
6	garlic cloves, chopped	6
4	medium mushrooms, chopped	4
210 ml (7¹/₂ fl oz)	olive oil	1 cup
pinch	cayenne pepper	pinch
6 twists	black pepper	6 twists
	sea salt to taste	
2 tbsp	tomato purée (paste)	2 tbsp
140 g (5 oz)	pine nuts and almond flakes, mixed	1 cup
4 tbsp	black raisins	4 tbsp
1	large potato	1
120 ml (4 fl oz)	olive oil	¹/₂ cup

1) Remove the ends of the aubergines (eggplants) and wash thoroughly. Slice the top lengthways.
2) Using a knife and spoon, empty the inside, taking care not to damage the skin.
3) Chop the aubergine (eggplant) flesh into small pieces and place in a saucepan together with rice, herbs, tomatoes, onions, garlic, mushrooms, 1 cup of oil, seasoning and tomato purée (paste). Add 1 litre (1¹/₂ pints/4 cups) of cold water, stir well and bring to the boil.
4) Cook for 45 minutes, stirring periodically (cook for longer if consistency is watery).
5) Remove from the heat, add the pine nuts, almonds and raisins. Mix together.
6) Meanwhile, season the aubergine (eggplant) with salt and pepper. If dark liquid is in the shells this can be ignored or rinsed out.
7) Stuff the aubergines (eggplants) with the mixture and replace the sliced top. Peel the potato and cut into thick segments and place between the aubergines (eggplants). Pour the remainder of the olive oil and 210 ml (7¹/₂ fl oz/ 1 cup) of water over the stuffed aubergines (eggplants) and season to taste.
8) Cover with foil and place into a preheated oven at 190°C/375°F/Gas Mark 5.
9) Remove the foil after 30 minutes and bake for a further 45 minutes or until all of the liquid has evaporated.

Rainbow Vegetable Grill

Serves 2

Metric (Imperial)		American
5 twists	black pepper	5 twists
	sea salt to taste	
2 tbsp	lemon juice	2 tbsp
1 tsp	oregano	1 tsp
60 ml (2 fl oz)	olive oil	1/4 cup
1	small red (bell) pepper	1
1	small green (bell) pepper	1
2	medium open mushrooms	2
1	medium onion, halved	1
2	small tomatoes	2
1	medium potato, pre-boiled	1
1	corn on the cob, pre-boiled	1
200 g (7 oz)	tofu, cubed (optional)	1 cup

1) Prepare the vegetables – halve the peppers lengthways, clean the mushrooms and discard the stalks, halve the tomato, cutting across, cut the corn in half lengthways and cut the potato in half.

2) In a bowl mix all of the seasonings together (pepper, salt, lemon juice, oregano and lemon juice).
3) Into this mixture dip all of the vegetables, ensuring they are completely covered before placing them under the grill.
4) Allow 5 minutes of cooking on each side – apart from the corn which should be grilled on one side only.
5) Serve with any savoury dish.
6) If tofu cubes are added to this recipe (cubed, covered in dressing, grilled) this becomes a main course.

Rice and Spinach with Garlic and Herbs

Serves 3 to 4

Metric (Imperial)		American
120 g (4 oz)	onion, chopped	1 cup
240 ml (8 fl oz)	olive or vegetable oil	1^1/$_2$ cups
880 g (32 oz)	spinach, well washed and cut into large pieces	16 cups
200 g (7 oz)	unpolished rice	1 cup
4	garlic cloves, sliced	4
60 g (2 oz)	spring onions (scallions), sliced	^{1}/$_2$ cup
60 g (2 oz)	dill, chopped	1 cup
60 g (2 oz)	parsley, chopped	1 cup
	sea salt to taste	
6 twists	black pepper	6 twists
30 ml (1 fl oz)	lemon juice	^{1}/$_8$ cup

1) Place the chopped onion into a saucepan with the oil and simmer until golden brown, then add the spinach.
2) Continue stirring until all of the spinach is lightly cooked at which time add 450 ml (15 fl oz/2 cups) of warm water plus the rice, garlic, spring onions (scallions), dill, parsley, salt and pepper.
3) Simmer for approximately 45 minutes, stirring regularly, until all the water has evaporated.

4) Test the rice to see if it is cooked, and if it is not, add a little warm water and continue to simmer until rice is soft.
5) Five minutes before removing from heat, when almost all the water had evaporated, add the lemon juice.
6) Alternatively, add the lemon juice to the dish when serving to enhance the flavour.

Pumpkin Pie (Savoury)

This dish is usually prepared using a white cheese and regular milk, however to avoid the undesirable animal fat and cholesterol sources we have substituted tofu (soya curd) and soya milk, and the results are excellent. Enjoy this traditional pie in a new, healthier form.

Serves 6

Metric (Imperial)		American
990 g (32 oz)	pumpkin, depipped and grated	5 cups
$^1/_2$ tsp	sea salt	$^1/_2$ tsp
455 g (16 oz)	tofu, crumbled	2 cups
210 ml ($7^1/_2$ fl oz)	soya milk	1 cup
110 g (5 oz)	rice flakes	$1^1/_2$ cups
85 g (3 oz)	almond flakes	1 cup
70 g ($2^1/_2$ oz)	pine kernels	$^1/_2$ cup
110 g (4 oz)	onion, grated	1 cup
30 g (1 oz)	parsley, chopped	$^1/_2$ cup
4	egg whites	4
120 ml (4 fl oz)	olive or vegetable oil	$^1/_2$ cup
1 packet	filo pastry leaves	1 packet

1) Remove the flesh of the pumpkin and grate this using the large holes on the grater. Place the grated pumpkin into a

colander and add the salt, mix well and allow to drain for 2 hours.

2) Squeeze the pumpkin by hand to extract the water and then place it into a bowl with all of the other ingredients apart from the egg whites. Mix well.

3) Beat the egg whites thoroughly and blend this by hand into the mixture.

4) Cover the inner surface and sides of a large ovenproof dish with filo pastry leaves. Oil the filo surface using a brush and add a second layer of filo. Repeat this process once more and then empty the pie mix into the oven dish, levelling with a spoon.

5) Place a top layer of filo, oil and cover with another layer and then repeat once more, so that there are effectively three layers of filo surrounding the pie on all sides. Paint a layer of oil onto the top of the upper layer of filo.

6) With a sharp knife score the upper surface to mark the portions of the pie in squares.

7) Bake in a preheated oven at 170°C/325°F/Gas Mark 3 until the surface is golden brown, which should take approximately 50 minutes.

8) Serve hot or cold.

Stuffed Cabbage Leaves

This tasty dish has excellent nutritional value. The béchamel sauce which is traditionally served with this dish contains egg yolks. In this recipe eggs can be used whole, just the egg whites, or the sauce can be avoided altogether. Anyone who is concerned about the 'egg-cholesterol' connection – which as explained in Chapter 3 – should be reminded that this is largely a fallacy – if the eggs are cooked in certain ways – and in the béchamel recipe the cooking is the 'safe' method. See page 163 for details of the making of the sauce.

Serves 4

Metric (Imperial)		American
200 g (7 oz)	brown rice	1 cup
1 tbsp	currants	1 tbsp
60 g (2 oz)	spring onions (scallions), chopped	¹/₂ cup
70 g (2¹/₂ oz)	pine kernels	¹/₂ cup
	sea salt to taste	
5 twists	black pepper	5 twists
210 ml (7¹/₂ fl oz)	olive oil	1 cup
1	egg white, beaten	1
45 g (1¹/₂ oz)	ground almonds	¹/₂ cup
30 g (1 oz)	parsley, chopped	¹/₂ cup
1	large savoy cabbage	1
210 ml (7¹/₂ fl oz)	lemon juice	1 cup

1) Boil the washed rice for 8 minutes then strain and place in a large mixing bowl.
2) Add the currants, spring onions (scallions), pine kernels, salt, black pepper, half the oil, the beaten egg white, almonds and parsley. Mix these ingredients well together.
3) Boil the cabbage for 2 to 3 minutes to soften the outer leaves. Remove from heat and separate the leaves.
4) Placing a tablespoon of the stuffing at the centre of each leaf, fold to envelope this before placing each envelope in a non-stick saucepan.
5) When all the stuffing is used chop the remaining leaves and spread them on top of the cabbage envelopes in the saucepan.
6) Place two small plates (saucers or side plates) on top of these leaves to ensure that they stay in place during the cooking process.
7) Add the remaining oil and the lemon juice to the saucepan and then enough additional water to ensure that the contents of the saucepan are covered with liquid. Bring to the boil and then simmer gently for 30 to 40 minutes until (by tipping the saucepan) there is no more than about one cupful of liquid remaining, at which time remove from heat and proceed to make the sauce (*see page 163*).
8) If no sauce is being made, allow the parcels to cook until almost all of the liquid has evaporated, remove from heat and serve. Alternatively cool and serve at room temperature, ideally accompanied by other cooked vegetables such as beans and/or courgettes (zucchini).

Sweet Potatoes and Okra (Ladies' Fingers)

Serves 2

Metric (Imperial)		American
180 ml (7 fl oz)	olive oil	$^2/_3$ cup
3	garlic cloves, chopped	3
1	chilli, sliced	1
200 g (7 oz)	okra (ladies' fingers)	4 cups
400 g (14 oz)	sweet potatoes, peeled and chopped	3 cups
100 g ($3^1/_2$ oz)	spinach, chopped	$1^3/_4$ cups
250 ml (8 fl oz)	vegetable stock	1 cup
6 twists	black pepper	6 twists
	sea salt to taste	
100 g ($3^1/_2$ oz)	French beans, topped and tailed and cut into 1 inch ($2^1/_2$ cm) lengths	1 cup
200 g (7 oz)	tofu, cubed (optional)	1 cup

1) In a shallow saucepan, place the olive oil together with the garlic, chilli and okra (ladies' fingers). Heat and stir for 5 minutes.
2) Add the sweet potatoes, spinach, stock and seasoning. Cook for 15 minutes.
3) Add the beans and cook for a further 7 minutes.

4) If all the liquid has evaporated and the potatoes are tender the dish is ready. If potatoes are not tender cook for a further few minutes until ready.

5) To turn this delicious side dish into a main course add tofu cubes in the last few minutes of cooking, or serve with fat-free cheese, and/or bread and walnuts.

Cook's Note

Before cooking okra (ladies' fingers) clean and sprinkle with salt and cider vinegar and leave in the sun for 2 hours, turning occasionally. This removes the slightly slimy texture of okra (ladies' fingers) and improves taste. It is not essential however.

Fish Dishes

Caribbean Baked Whitebait

Serves 2

Metric (Imperial)		American
455 g (1 lb)	whitebait	2²/₃ cups
	sea salt to taste	
5 twists	black pepper	5 twists
6	garlic cloves, halved	6
1	medium onion, chopped	1
200 ml (7 fl oz)	olive oil	³/₄ cup
	chilli pepper to taste	
1	large tomato, skinned and sliced	1

1) Wash the fish well.
2) Season with salt and pepper and refrigerate for 1 hour.
3) Arrange the fish evenly in a baking dish, and add the garlic, onion, olive oil and chilli pepper.

4) Half cover with slices of tomato, adding approximately 150ml (5 fl oz/²/₃ cup) of water.
5) Bake in a preheated oven at 190°C/375°F/Gas Mark 5 for approximately 30 minutes or until all the liquid has evaporated.
6) Serve with green salad.

Cod Baked with Asparagus Spears

Serves 2

Metric (Imperial)		American
2	thick cod steaks	2
10	asparagus spears	10

Dressing

$^1/_2$ tsp	salt	$^1/_2$ tsp
6 twists	black pepper	6 twists
pinch	cayenne pepper	pinch
4 tbsp	olive oil	4 tbsp
3 tbsp	lemon juice	3 tbsp
1	garlic clove, crushed	1

1) Mix the dressing ingredients in a small bowl.
2) Wash and pat dry the thick cod steaks and place them in a baking dish.
3) Surround the steaks with the well-washed asparagus.
4) Pour the dressing over the fish and asparagus and turn the fish to ensure that all sides are covered.
5) Bake in a preheated oven at 190°C/375°F/Gas Mark 5 for approximately 20 minutes.

Corfu Grilled Sardines

Serves 2

Metric (Imperial)	American	
8	large, fresh sardines	8
1 tsp	oregano	1 tsp
120 ml (4 fl oz)	olive oil	$^1/_2$ cup
2 tbsp	lemon juice	2 tbsp
5 twists	black pepper	5 twists
	sea salt to taste	

1) Scrape off the scales and remove the heads from the fish. Place into a shallow bowl.
2) Separately mix the remaining ingredients. Pour half of this mixture onto the sardines.
3) Ensure the sardines are evenly covered and refrigerate for 1 hour.
4) Meanwhile, preheat the grill. Grill the sardines for 5 minutes on either side.
5) When cooked, spoon the remaining mixture onto the fish.
6) Serve with a salad of your choice.

Grey Mullet with Garlic and Lemon

Serves 2

Metric (Imperial)		American
2	grey mullets	2
	sea salt to taste	
200 ml (7 fl oz)	lemon juice	$^3/_4$ cup
175 g (6 oz)	carrots, cut lengthways	$1^1/_2$ cups
5	garlic cloves, chopped	5
60 g (2 oz)	parsley, chopped	1 cup
210 ml (7 fl oz)	olive oil	1 cup
2	medium onions, cut lengthways	2
4 twists	black pepper	4 twists
425 ml (15 fl oz)	water	2 cups

1) Wash and clean the fish.
2) Place the mullets on a plate, sprinkle the sea salt over them and pour over half of the lemon juice.
3) Turn the fish to ensure it is well dressed with the lemon juice.
4) Cover with foil and refrigerate for 45 minutes.
5) In a shallow saucepan, add the vegetables and all the other ingredients to the fish.
6) Bring to the boil and then allow to simmer, shaking gently from time to time, until all the water has evaporated, approximately 30 minutes.

Oven Baked Salmon and Squash

Serves 2

Metric (Imperial)		American
2	salmon steaks	2
2 tbsp	lemon juice	2 tbsp
5 tbsp	olive oil	5 tbsp
6 twists	black pepper	6 twists
	sea salt to taste	
1	medium squash	1
	or	
2 slices	pumpkin	2 slices
6	garlic cloves	6

1) Wash and pat dry the salmon. Place in a baking dish and add the lemon juice, oil and seasoning. Refrigerate for 1 hour.
2) Peel and slice the pumpkin or squash, discarding the seeds.
3) Cut into large pieces and arrange around the fish. Add the garlic.
4) Turn the fish over and ensure that the squash or pumpkin pieces have been dressed with the oil and lemon mixture.
5) Add 4 tablespoons of water and bake for 30 minutes in a preheated oven at 180°C/350°F/Gas Mark 4.
6) Serve with salad or cooked vegetables. For a delicious accompaniment, try the Garlic Potato (*see page 58*) or Walnut and Garlic Dip (*see page 61*).

Salmon Patties

Serves 4

Metric (Imperial)		American
475 g (1 lb)	tinned salmon	2²/₃ cups
4	egg whites	4
5 tbsp	oat cereal	5 tbsp
1	medium onion, finely grated	1
1 tbsp	parsley, finely chopped	1 tsp
1 tbsp	lemon juice	1 tbsp

1) Mix all ingredients together and form into burger-shaped patties.
2) Brush the surface of a frying pan with olive oil and fry until the patties are crisp on the outside.
3) Serve with the rice or mashed potatoes or salad.

Salmon Poached with Garlic and Lemon

Salmon is a highly nutritious fish containing many of the essential fatty acids which have an anti-inflammatory effect. Poaching is an ideal way of preparing fish. Serve this with a side salad and/or cooked vegetables dressed with lemon juice and olive oil.

Serves 2

Metric (Imperial)		American
450 g (16 oz)	2 x salmon steaks or fillets	2 cups

Dressing

Metric (Imperial)		American
	salt to taste	
90 ml (3 fl oz)	olive oil	$^1/_3$ cup
4 tbsp	lemon juice	4 tbsp
3	garlic cloves, crushed	3
3 twists	black pepper	3 twists
pinch	cayenne pepper	pinch

1) Wash and pat dry the fish. On a plate, sprinkle a little salt on both sides of the fish, cover with foil and refrigerate for 1 hour.

2) Mix all of the dressing ingredients in a cup.

3) Fill a saucepan with sufficient water to cover the fish. Bring the water to the boil, adding a little salt.

4) When the water is boiling, place the fish into it (ensuring it is completely covered) and simmer for 10 to 15 minutes (cod steaks take longer than cod fillets).

5) Remove from heat and drain the water from the fish.

6) Pour on the dressing and serve.

Poultry Dishes

Ginger and Garlic Spiced Chicken

Poultry is excellent for a cholesterol-controlled diet, as long as the skin is removed, as this is where the fat is concentrated. If at all possible, obtain free-range poultry, which has not been exposed to antibiotic or steroid medication. By combining the chicken with ginger and garlic we ensure extra health benefits – as well as flavour!

Serves 2

Metric (Imperial)		American
450 g (16 oz)	boneless, skinless chicken thighs	2 cups
140 ml (5 fl oz)	olive oil	$^2/_3$ cup
5	garlic cloves	5
85 g (3 oz)	root ginger, freshly grated	$^1/_2$ cup
1	juice of 1 lemon	1
pinch	cayenne pepper	pinch

5 twists	black pepper	5 twists
	salt to taste	
675 ml (24 fl oz)	hot water	3 cups

1) Place the chicken thighs into a shallow saucepan, together with the olive oil.
2) Heat gently and stir frequently for 10 to 15 minutes and then add the remaining ingredients (except for the water), stirring constantly for a minute.
3) Add 450 ml (16 fl oz/2 cups) of hot water and cover. Simmer gently until the water has almost evaporated at which time add a further 225 ml (8 fl oz/1 cup) of hot water and cook for a further 10 minutes.
4) Serve with any vegetables or fresh salads with a rice based side dish.

Greek-Style Chicken Roast

Serves 2

Metric (Imperial)		American
2 portions	roasting chicken, skin removed	2 portions
6	garlic cloves, with skin	6
2	medium potatoes	2
120 ml (4 fl oz)	olive oil	$^1/_2$ cup
$^1/_2$ tsp	oregano	$^1/_2$ tsp
2 tbsp	lemon juice	2 tbsp
pinch	powdered chilli pepper	pinch
5 twists	black pepper	5 twists
	sea salt to taste	

1) Remove all of the fat and skin from the chicken, wash well and place into a roasting tin.
2) Peel the potatoes and cut into segments, and arrange around the chicken pieces.
3) Mix all of the other ingredients in a separate bowl. Pour this over the chicken and potatoes. Ensure that the chicken is well covered with mixture.
4) Add 150 ml ($^1/_4$ pint/$^2/_3$ cup) of water. Cover with foil and place into a preheated oven at 190°C/375°F/Gas Mark 5.

5) Bake for 30 minutes then remove the foil and continue to bake until the water has evaporated (approximately 20 minutes).
6) Serve with salad or vegetables.

Spicy Oriental Turkey Burgers

Serves 4

Metric (Imperial)		American
450 g (1 lb)	ground turkey breast	2 cups
4 tbsp	oat cereal	4 tbsp
1 tbsp	soy sauce	1 tbsp
28 g (1 oz)	fresh ginger, finely grated	1 level tbsp
$1/2$ tsp	ground coriander	$1/2$ tsp
60 g (2 oz)	shiitake (or other) mushrooms, finely chopped	$2/3$ cup
1 tsp	salt	1 tsp

1) Mix all of the ingredients and form four burger-shaped patties.
2) Place under a preheated grill and cook until brown, turn and cook the other side.
3) Serve with rice, stir-fried vegetables and soy sauce (if desired).

Turkey Burgers

Serves 4

Metric (Imperial)		American
450 g (1 lb)	ground turkey breast	2 cups
4 tbsp	oat cereal	4 tbsp
2	garlic cloves, crushed	2
1	small onion, chopped	1
1	small green (bell) pepper, chopped	1
1 tsp	salt	1 tsp
4 twists	black pepper	4 twists

1) Mix all of the ingredients and form four burger-shaped patties.
2) Place under a preheated grill and cook until brown, turn and cook the other side.
3) Serve on toasted sourdough buns (which are low in fat) with lettuce, tomato slices, onion rings (raw or lightly stir-fried).

Stir-Fried Chicken and Vegetables

Serves 2

Metric (Imperial)		American
180 g (6 oz)	chicken pieces, preboiled and cubed	1¹/₂ cups
30 g (1 oz)	cashew nuts	¹/₄ cup
2 tbsp	olive or safflower oil	2 tbsp
2	small carrots, sliced thinly lengthways	2
1	courgette (zucchini), sliced	1
2	celery sticks, sliced	2
3	spring onions (scallions), chopped	3
120 g (4 oz)	mushrooms, sliced	1 cup
120 g (4 oz)	mangetout	1 cup
1 tbsp	grated root ginger	1 tbsp

1) Place the chicken cubes into a saucepan, cover with water and bring to the boil and cook for 10 minutes.
2) Meanwhile place the nuts into either a wok or a deep frying pan and dry roast these for a few minutes until they darken in colour. Use a wooden spoon to stir them, to prevent burning.
3) Remove the nuts and put them on a plate to cool.

4) Very lightly oil the pan using half the oil suggested and stir-fry the carrots for 1 minute before adding the rest of the vegetables, the boiled chicken cubes and the remaining oil (but not the ginger).
5) Constantly stir the ingredients as they cook for a further 1 to 2 minutes.
6) Add the grated root ginger and the nuts and cook for a further 30 seconds before turning out the contents into a serving bowl or platter.
7) Serve with rice.

Cook's Note

If you enjoy an even stronger taste of ginger you might want to add a teaspoon or two of ginger purée to the cooking vegetables.

Chicken Fillets and Baked Apple

Serves 2

Metric (Imperial)		American
2	chicken fillets, skin and fat removed	2
$^1/_2$ tsp	oregano	$^1/_2$ tsp
4 tbsp	olive oil	4 tbsp
2 tbsp	lemon juice	2 tbsp
4	garlic cloves, chopped	4
	black pepper to taste	
	salt to taste	
2	cooking apples, cores removed	2

1) Place all of the ingredients except the apples into a baking dish.
2) Mix to ensure fillets have been in touch with all other ingredients.
3) Add 200ml (7 fl oz/$^3/_4$ cup) of water.
4) Cover with foil and place in a preheated oven at 190°C/375°F/Gas Mark 3 and bake for 25 minutes.
5) Remove the foil, add the apples and bake for a further 30 minutes.
6) Serve with a salad such as the Root Salad (*see page 75*).

Side Dishes

Artichoke Meze

Serves 5

Metric (Imperial)		American
10	small tender artichokes	10
1	lemon, juiced	1
$^1/_2$ tsp	sea salt	$^1/_2$ tsp
140 g (5 oz)	85% self-raising flour	1 cup
1	egg white	1
240 ml (8 fl oz)	warm water	1 cup
180 ml (7$^1/_2$ fl oz)	olive oil	1 cup

1) Prepare the artichokes (*see page 38*) – remove all the outer leaves and detach the top. Cut in half and remove the choke.

2) Dip an artichoke half in lemon juice and place into a saucepan covered with water. Repeat with remaining artichokes.
3) When all of the artichokes have been prepared, rinse thoroughly under running water.
4) Bring a saucepan containing 1 litre (1½ pints/4 cups) of water to the boil, add ½ teaspoon of salt, place the artichoke halves into this and cook until tender (approximately 30 minutes).
5) Remove, drain and allow to cool.
6) Meanwhile, prepare the batter using the flour, egg white and water. Dip the artichokes in the batter.
7) Heat the oil in a frying pan, then add the artichoke halves, one at a time, into the pan. Fry until golden.
8) Serve hot or cold as an appetizer (Greek Meze) or side dish.

Baked Garlic

Serves 2

Metric (Imperial)		American
12	large garlic cloves, in skin	12
60 ml (2 fl oz)	olive oil	$^1/_4$ cup
2 tbsp	lemon juice	2 tbsp
5 twists	black pepper	5 twists
	sea salt to taste	

1) Arrange the garlic cloves (with skin) in a baking dish.
2) Add the rest of the ingredients and toss, adding 50 ml (2 fl oz / $^1/_2$ cup) of water.
3) Place in a preheated oven at 180°C/350°F/Gas Mark 4 and bake for 30 minutes.
4) Serve as an accompaniment to any savoury recipes, especially fish.

Baked Onions

Serves 1 or 2

Metric (Imperial)		American
2 tbsp	olive oil	2 tbsp
1 tbsp	cider vinegar	1 tbsp
6 twists	black pepper	6 twists
	sea salt to taste	
2	medium onions	2

1) Place all of the ingredients (except the onions) into a bowl and mix well.
2) Remove the core from the onions, 2½ cm (1 inch) deep, without going all the way through.
3) Brush the surface of the onions with the mixture, then pour a tablespoon of the mixture inside.
4) Place the onions into a baking dish, cover with foil and bake until tender at 180°C/350°F/Gas Mark 4 – for 1 hour.
5) Serve with any savoury dish.

Button Mushrooms with Ginger

Serves 2 to 3

Metric (Imperial)		American
455 g (1 lb)	firm fresh button mushrooms	4 cups
1	medium onion, chopped	1
1	medium carrot, diced	1
4	garlic cloves, chopped	4
2 tbsp	tomato purée (paste)	2 tbsp
1½ tbsp	freshly grated ginger	1½ tbsp
30 ml (1 fl oz)	olive oil	⅛ cup
5 twists	black pepper	5 twists
	sea salt to taste	
4 tbsp	white wine	4 tbsp

1) Wash the mushrooms well and place in a saucepan along with the other ingredients (apart from the wine) plus 250 ml (½ pint/1⅓ cups) water.
2) Bring to the boil and cook on a medium heat until almost all of the water has evaporated (approximately 45 minutes).
3) Add the wine and stir. Shake the saucepan and cook for 10 more minutes or until all the liquid has evaporated.
4) Serve with any savoury dish.

Couscous with Almonds

Serves 2

Metric (Imperial)		American
225 g (8 oz)	couscous	1^1/$_3$ cups
6 twists	black pepper	6 twists
	sea salt to taste	
3 tbsp	almond flakes	3 tbsp
1	celery stalk, chopped	1
^{1}/$_2$	apple, peeled and diced	^{1}/$_2$
2 tbsp	olive oil	2 tbsp
1	small tomato, peeled and diced	1
340 ml (12 fl oz)	boiling water	1^1/$_2$ cups

1) Place the couscous into a saucepan and add the seasoning.
2) Pour boiling water onto the couscous, stir and cover. Leave to stand for 15 minutes.
3) Uncover and with a fork, stir to fluff the couscous mixture.
4) Add the other ingredients to the couscous, toss and serve.
5) Accompanies almost any meal, hot or cold, as a salad with savoury meals or with other salads.

Fried Aubergine (Eggplant)

Serves 2

Metric (Imperial)		American
1	large aubergine (eggplant)	1
generous pinch	sea salt	generous pinch
240 ml (8 fl oz)	olive oil	1 cup
6	garlic cloves	6
2 tbsp	cider vinegar	2 tbsp

1) Wash and slice the aubergine (eggplant) to 1 cm ($\frac{1}{2}$ inch) thickness.
2) Place these in layers in a colander, sprinkling salt on the upper surface of each segment before covering with the next. Leave to stand for 20 minutes.
3) Blue fluid will appear on the surface of the vegetable – the bitterness of the aubergine (eggplant) is being removed by the salt. Rinse each slice individually and then squeeze out all excess fluid and pat dry with absorbent kitchen paper.
4) Meanwhile, heat the oil in a frying pan. When hot, place the aubergine (eggplant) segments into the pan, with as much surface touching the pan as possible.
5) After 2 minutes the aubergine (eggplant) should be golden brown. Turn over and fry the other side.

6) When both sides are golden brown, remove from the frying pan and place onto a plate.
7) Repeat until all slices are cooked.
8) While the last slices of aubergine (eggplant) are cooking, add the peeled, whole garlic to the pan.
9) Remove the last aubergine (eggplant) slices (but not the garlic) and add the vinegar and immediately pour this (and the garlic) over the previously fried aubergines (eggplants). Take care as the vinegar could splash and/or smoke.
10) Serve hot or cold as an accompaniment to fish or any other savoury meal.

Green Beans with Garlic

Serves 2 to 3

Metric (Imperial)		American
	sea salt to taste	
425 g (1 lb)	green beans, topped and tailed	5 cups
30 g (1 oz)	parsley, chopped	$^1/_2$ cup
1 tbsp	garlic, crushed	1 tbsp
140 ml (5 fl oz)	olive oil	$^2/_3$ cup
70 ml ($2^1/_2$ fl oz)	cider vinegar	$^1/_3$ cup
4 twists	black pepper	4 twists

1) In a saucepan add the sea salt to 1 litre (2 pints/5 cups) of water and bring to the boil.
2) Place the beans in the saucepan and cook for 10 minutes (or longer if you prefer them soft).
3) Meanwhile, in a bowl place the remaining ingredients and mix well to make a sauce.
4) When the beans are cooked, drain well.
5) Put the beans into a serving dish and pour the sauce over.
6) Serve warm or at room temperature. Ideal with any fish, poultry or vegetarian savoury.

New Potatoes with Basil or Mint

Serves 2 to 4

Metric (Imperial)		American
455 g (1 lb)	new baby potatoes, washed and scrubbed	3 cups
	sea salt to taste	
60 g (2 oz)	basil or mint leaves	2 cups
140 ml (5fl oz)	olive oil	$^2/_3$ cup
2 tbsp	cider vinegar	2 tbsp
8 twists	black pepper	8 twists
10	black olives	10

1) Place the new potatoes in a saucepan and cover with water.
2) Add sea salt to taste and $^1/_3$ of the leaves. Bring to the boil and cook until the potatoes are tender (approximately 40 minutes).
3) Drain the potatoes, add the other ingredients and mix carefully but well.
4) Place into a serving bowl and serve warm.

Oven Roasted Garlic

Serves 4

Metric (Imperial)		American
4	medium to large heads of garlic	4
85 ml (3 fl oz)	olive oil	$^1/_3$ cup
220 ml (7$^1/_2$ fl oz)	water	1 cup

1) Chop the top off the head of garlic to expose the inner cloves. Place the garlic heads in a shallow dish (or a special 'garlic baker' if you have one).
2) Brush the tops with olive oil.
3) Fill the dish with 2$^1/_2$ cm (1 inch) of water and cover with the lid or foil.
4) Bake in a preheated oven at 200°C/400°F/Gas Mark 6 for 1 hour or until the garlic is light brown and soft.
5) Serve with warm bread which has previously been lightly brushed with virgin olive oil. Remove the garlic 'pulp' and spread onto the bread.

Spicy Brussels Sprouts

Serves 2 to 3

Metric (Imperial)		American
455 g (1 lb)	fresh Brussels sprouts	4 cups
2	medium sized potatoes	2
1	medium onion, chopped	1
115 ml (4 fl oz)	olive oil	$^1/_2$ cup
pinch	cayenne pepper	pinch
$1^1/_2$ tbsp	tomato purée (paste)	$1^1/_2$ tbsp
5 twists	black pepper	5 twists
	sea salt to taste	
1 tbsp	lemon juice	1 tbsp

1) Prepare the sprouts by cleaning and removing the damaged outer leaves.
2) Peel the potatoes and cut into quarters. Place into a saucepan with the sprouts. Add the other ingredients apart from the lemon juice, and cover with water.
3) Bring to the boil and cook until most of the water has evaporated (approximately 40 minutes).
4) Add lemon juice while still on the heat, shaking saucepan to agitate the ingredients, and cook for a further 5 minutes.
5) Remove and serve. Ideal with any savoury dishes.

Stewed Aubergines (Eggplants)

Serves 2

Metric (Imperial)		American
1	medium onion, chopped	1
450 ml (16 fl oz)	water	2 cups
2 tbsp	flat-leaf parsley, chopped	2 tbsp
240 ml (8 fl oz)	olive oil	1 cup
450 g (16 oz)	tinned (canned) tomatoes	2 cups
1 tbsp	tomato purée (paste)	1 tbsp
4	garlic cloves, chopped	4
8 twists	black pepper	8 twists
pinch	cayenne pepper	pinch
	sea salt to taste	
240 g (8 oz)	tofu (soya curd) cubes (optional)	1 cup
2	medium aubergines (eggplants)	2
4 tbsp	white wine	4 tbsp

1) Place all of the ingredients except for the aubergines (eggplants), tofu and wine into a shallow saucepan. Mix with a wooden spoon.

2) Stew until the ingredients are soft (approximately 30 minutes).

3) Meanwhile prepare the aubergines (eggplants). Discard the stalk end then wash the aubergines (eggplants). Cut into 4cm (1½ inch) thick segments (cutting across not lengthways).

4) After approximately 30 minutes, add the wine to the saucepan and stir.

5) Now add the aubergine (eggplant) segments into saucepan.

6) Ensure all pieces are covered by the sauce as it cooks, and if necessary add a cup of boiling water. Shake the pan and allow to slowly stew until all of the water has evaporated (approximately 40 minutes).

7) Serve as a side dish to accompany any savoury meal, or turn this into a main course by adding cubes of tofu 5 minutes before the completion of cooking, ensuring that the tofu is completely covered by the sauce.

Stuffed Onions

Serves 2

Metric (Imperial)		American
2	large onions	2
3 tbsp	black raisins	3 tbsp
2 tbsp	walnuts, broken	2 tbsp
2 tbsp	cider vinegar	2 tbsp
4 twists	black pepper	4 twists
	sea salt to taste	

1) Peel the onions and with a grapefruit knife remove the core without breaking through the other end. Discard the core.
2) In a bowl, place the other ingredients and mix well.
3) With this mixture stuff the onions.
4) Place the stuffed onions into a small baking dish and add 240 ml (8 fl oz/1 cup) of cold water.
5) Preheat the oven to 190°C/375°F/Gas Mark 5 and bake for 50 minutes.
6) Serve with any hot savoury meal.

Sweet Potatoes and Leeks

Serves 2

Metric (Imperial)		American
1	large sweet potato	1
4	small leeks	4
1	medium onion, chopped	1
60 ml (2 fl oz)	olive oil	$^{1}/_{4}$ cup
$1^{1}/_{2}$ tbsp	tomato purée (paste)	$1^{1}/_{2}$ tbsp
pinch	chilli pepper	pinch
6 twists	black pepper	6 twists
	sea salt to taste	

1) Prepare the vegetables. Cut the leaks into 5 cm (2 inch) pieces. Peel the sweet potato and slice into $2^{1}/_{2}$ cm (1 inch) thick discs. Rinse and place into a saucepan with the other ingredients.
2) Cover with water and cook on a moderate heat until all of the water has evaporated (approximately 45 minutes).
3) Ideal as an accompaniment to fish or chicken dishes.

Cook's Note

Ideally the sweet potatoes should be those with a white flesh rather than the orange coloured ones which aren't as firm once cooked.

Tenderized Spinach and Garlic

This dish is very quick to prepare and also one of the most delicious, nutritious and addictive healthy meals imaginable.

Serves 1

Metric (Imperial)		American
60 ml (2 fl oz)	olive oil	$^1/_4$ cup
10	garlic cloves, whole or halved	10
440 g (16 oz)	spinach, well washed and cut or torn by hand into large pieces	16 cups
	sea salt to taste	
	ground black pepper to taste (after cooking)	

1) Lightly oil a large frying pan.
2) Place on a very high heat and immediately add the garlic and cook, stirring frequently, for about 1 minute – just long enough to tenderize the cloves.
3) Add the spinach and a little salt and agitate while this slightly tenderizes – for no more than 45 seconds (30 seconds is usually enough).
4) Serve while hot with a few twists of black pepper and enjoy the absolutely fabulous texture and taste.

5) Accompany with fresh, crusty, Italian bread and olive oil to make this a fully satisfying light meal.

Tomatoes Provençal

Serves 2

Metric (Imperial)		American
4	medium size tomatoes	4
1	spring onion (scallion)	1
3	garlic cloves, chopped	3
2 tbsp	olive oil	2 tbsp
25 g (1 oz)	blackcurrants (optional)	$^1/_4$ cup
	salt and pepper to taste	
30 g (1 oz)	parsley, chopped	$^1/_2$ cup

1) Wash the tomatoes and cut across the top. Scoop out the contents using a teaspoon or grapefruit knife, taking care not to damage the skin.
2) Chop the tomato contents. Add to all the other ingredients (reserve a little of the parsley for garnish) and mix well.
3) Stuff the tomatoes with this mixture and place in a baking dish.
4) Bake in a preheated oven at 200°C/400°F/Gas Mark 6 for 45 minutes.
5) Just before serving, garnish the tomatoes with the retained parsley.
6) Ideal as a side dish or as a starter.

Sauces and Dressings

Dairy-Free Béchamel Sauce

This sauce can be used with Artichoke Moussaka (*see page 97*)
or Stuffed Cabbage Leaves (*see page 122*).

Metric (Imperial)		American
4 tbsp	self-raising flour	4 tbsp
120 ml (4 fl oz)	olive oil	¹/₂ cup
425 ml (15 fl oz)	oat or soya milk	2 cups
240 ml (8 fl oz)	stock from cooked artichokes (or any vegetable)	1 cup
2	eggs or egg whites, lightly beaten	2
5 twists	black pepper	5 twists
	sea salt to taste	

1) Place the flour and oil into a frying pan on a medium heat and stir constantly until they are well mixed.
2) Alternately add to this a small amount of soya milk and the vegetable water until these are used up.
3) Stir constantly with a wooden spoon to ensure the ingredients are blended as the liquids are slowly added.
4) Once the milk has been absorbed, if the texture is too thick, add a little more oat/soya milk until a smooth, thick texture has been achieved.
5) Remove from the heat and add the eggs, stirring constantly until well mixed.
6) Season and use immediately.

Pine Nut and Almond Pesto Sauce

This remarkable variation on traditional pesto – avoiding the high fat cheese commonly used in the recipe – can be used in rice, pasta and vegetable dishes.

Serves 3 to 4

Metric (Imperial)		American
60 g (2 oz)	fresh basil	2 cups
60 g (2 oz)	fresh parsley	1 cup
70 g (2$^{1}/_{2}$ oz)	pine kernels	$^{1}/_{2}$ cup
85 g (3 oz)	ground almonds	1 cup
180 ml (6 fl oz)	olive oil	$^{2}/_{3}$ cup
	sea salt to taste	
4 twists	black pepper	4 twists
5	garlic cloves, crushed	5

1) The basil and parsley should be well washed and finely chopped in a food processor.
2) Separately chop the pine kernels in a food processor.
3) Place the basil, parsley, processed pine kernels and the ground almonds into a blender, together with the oil, salt, pepper and crushed garlic and blend these into a thick sauce.
4) If using the pesto as a spaghetti sauce, cook the pasta (whole wheat, rice, soy, millet pastas are now available – some with a low salt content) and drain.

5) Put the spaghetti back into the saucepan together with half of the pesto sauce and mix gently but thoroughly. Serve on a platter after adding the remainder of the pesto sauce.

Mushroom and Garlic Sauce

This sauce is an ideal base from which variations can be created for use with brown rice or wholemeal pasta dishes. Since pasta is now made from food sources other than wheat – such as rice, corn, and soya – wheat sensitive people can enjoy marvellous Mediterranean dishes without aggravating their conditions. If desired tomato purée (paste) can be added for additional flavour.

Serves 4

Metric (Imperial)		American
920 g (2 lb)	whole button mushrooms	8 cups
2	medium onions, quartered	2
6	garlic cloves, whole	6
2 tsp	dried basil	2 tsp
285 ml (10 fl oz)	olive oil	1¹/₂ cups
2	bay leaves, crushed	2
¹/₄ tsp	cayenne pepper	¹/₄ tsp
120 ml (4 fl oz)	dry white wine	¹/₂ cup
5 twists	black pepper	5 twists
425 ml (15 fl oz)	cold water	2 cups
	sea salt to taste	
4 tbsp	tomato purée (paste) (optional)	4 tbsp

1) Wash mushrooms thoroughly. Place in a processor and reduce to large breadcrumb size. Place the chopped mushrooms into a saucepan.
2) In a food processor, reduce the onions, garlic, basil, bay leaves to a cream-like consistency.
3) Add this to the mushrooms, together with the remaining ingredients, including the tomato purée (paste) if desired. Mix well.
4) Bring to the boil and simmer on a low heat until all of the water evaporates (approximately 40 minutes).
5) Serve hot with pasta or rice.

Cook's Note

Any unused sauce can be frozen. If cheese is allowed in your diet, then a sprinkling of hard low-fat cheese can be added before serving.

Garlic and Cider Vinegar Dressing

3 large salads or 6 side salads

Metric (Imperial)		American
3 tbsp	cider vinegar	3 tbsp
1 tbsp	fresh basil, parsley or thyme, chopped or	1 tbsp
1 tsp	dried marjoram or tarragon	1 tsp
2	garlic cloves, crushed	2
1 tsp	French mustard	1 tsp
	salt substitute to taste	
3 twists	black pepper	3 twists
85 ml (3 fl oz)	cold pressed virgin olive oil	⅓ cup

1) Mix together the cider vinegar with the herbs, crushed garlic, mustard, salt substitute and the pepper.
2) Blend in the oil and add to salad.

Mint and Honey Salad Dressing

This dressing was devised by Dr Boris Chaitow, the famous pioneer of dietary health promotion, for use on the vast salads he ate daily throughout his almost 90 years of active life.

Serves 1

Metric (Imperial)		American
3 tbsp	sunflower oil	3 tbsp
1 tbsp	lemon juice	1 tbsp
1 tsp	honey	1 tsp
2	garlic cloves, crushed	2
2 tbsp	mint leaves chopped	2 tbsp

1) Mix the oil and lemon juice in a bowl.
2) Dissolve the honey in a cup with a little hot water and then add it to the oil and lemon mixture together with the crushed garlic and the chopped mint leaves.
3) Mix thoroughly and keep refrigerated until required.

Vinaigrette

Metric (Imperial)		American
90 ml (3 fl oz)	olive oil	$^1/_3$ cup
2 tbsp	cider vinegar	2 tbsp
1 tsp	demerara sugar	1 tsp
1 tsp	mustard	1 tsp
	seasoning to taste	

1) Mix all of the ingredients together and pour onto salad.

Desserts

Berry and Nuts Delight

This berry and nut mix contains enormous amounts of flavonoids which have antioxidant (protective) influences on cardiovascular health. The nuts offer their own benefits in a cholesterol-controlled diet.

Serves 2

Metric (Imperial)		American
3 tbsp	fresh strawberries, chopped	3 tbsp
3 tbsp	fresh blueberries	3 tbsp
3 tbsp	raspberries	3 tbsp
3 tbsp	blackberries	3 tbsp
250 ml (8 fl oz)	fat-free or soya yogurt	1 cup
3 tbsp	almond flakes	3 tbsp
3 tbsp	broken walnuts	3 tbsp

1) Carefully wash the berries and allow to drain.
2) Place in a flattish bowl and add the yogurt. Sprinkle nuts over the yogurt.

Cook's Note

As an alternative to yogurt, pour the juice of 1–2 oranges over the fruit and nuts before serving.

Quince with Nuts and Pomegranate

This winter dessert derives from those climes where quince grows widely, southern Europe. This neglected fruit is now generally but seasonably (late autumn and early winter months) available from specialist green grocers and ethnic stores. If a large quince is chosen this dish can often become a meal in itself. The use of a small amount of thick yogurt (plain, live, no fat) enhances the wonderful quince flavours but this should be avoided if dairy foods are likely to cause sensitivity reactions.

Serves 1

Metric (Imperial)		American
1	medium to large qunice	1
85 g (3 oz)	fresh walnuts, shelled	1 cup
5 tbsp	pomegranate seeds	5 tbsp
30 g (1 oz)	low or no fat, plain, plain live yogurt (optional)	$1/4$ cup
1 tsp	honey (optional)	1 tsp

1) Wash the quince and place it in a preheated oven at 150°C/300°F/Gas Mark 2, for 45 minutes.
2) Remove from the heat and slice the quince open, discarding the core and seeds.

3) Serve with the nuts (which complement the taste wonderfully) and the pomegranate seeds.

4) If desired, the yogurt and/or the honey can be used to dress the dish before serving.

Cook's Note

The honey modifies the slightly sharp taste of quince, however the nuts and pomegranate seeds will also achieve this without raising sugar levels.

Greek Tzaleti (Nut Pancake)

Serves 2 to 3

Metric (Imperial)		American
225 g (8 oz)	85% self-raising flour	1¹/₂ cups
500 ml (16 fl oz)	undiluted soya milk	2 cups
1	egg	1
pinch	salt	pinch
1 tbsp	olive oil	1 tbsp
140 ml (5 fl oz)	olive oil, for frying	²/₃ cup
1 tbsp per pancake	broken walnuts or almond flakes	1 tbsp per pancake
pinch per serving	ground cinnamon	pinch per serving
1 tsp per serving	honey	1 tsp per serving

1) Place the flour into a large bowl. Slowly add the milk, stirring constantly with a wooden spoon.
2) Add the beaten egg and keep stirring until the texture is smooth and free of lumps. Add salt and a tablespoon of oil.
3) Heat the remaining olive oil in a large non-stick pan.
4) Using a large spoon place 6 or 7 individual spoonfuls of the mixture into the heated oil, to utilize as much of the pan as possible without allowing the individual pancakes to touch. After 1 minute turn them over.
5) Repeat turning until the surface is golden – almost brown.

6) Remove and place onto a plate lined with absorbent (kitchen) paper.
7) Continue cooking pancakes until all of the mixture has been used.
8) Serve while the pancakes are still warm. Add the nuts, sprinkle with cinnamon and a touch of honey (average portion as dessert is 3 to 4 pancakes).

Stuffed Pears

Serves 2

Metric (Imperial)		American
2	large ripe pears	2
1 tbsp	soaked raisins	1 tbsp
1 tbsp	walnuts, crushed	1 tbsp
1 tbsp	flaked almonds	1 tbsp
1 tbsp	fresh seasonal berries	1 tbsp
1 tbsp	fresh pineapple, diced	1 tbsp
4 tbsp	fat-free yogurt	4 tbsp

1) Peel and halve the pears, remove the cores. Place onto serving plates.
2) Mix all of the other ingredients except for the yogurt.
3) Fill each pear with the mixture.
4) Serve having added two tablespoons of yogurt to each pear.

Fat-Free Yogurt with Exotic Fruit

Serves 1

Metric (Imperial)		American
70 g (2½ oz)	each of dried mango, pineapple, blueberries	⅓ cup
150 g (5 oz)	fat-free plain yogurt	½ cup
60 g (2 oz)	mixed almond flakes and pumpkin seeds	½ cup

1) Cover the dried fruit with enough water and soak for at least 3 hours.
2) Drain any liquid and place in a dessert bowl. Add the yogurt, seeds and nuts.

Cook's Note

Dried fruits are available from many health stores and supermarkets. Use apricots, peaches etc. as alternatives.

Health Drinks

Cider Vinegar and Molasses

The health enhancing benefits of cider vinegar are well documented, helping to reduce acidity and to 'cleanse' the blood stream, according to 'folk medicine' traditions. Molasses of course have a high level of mineral nourishment and helps in bowel regularity.

Serves 1

Metric (Imperial)		American
1¹/₂ tsp	cider vinegar	1¹/₂ tsp
1¹/₂ tsp	molasses	1¹/₂ tsp
250 ml (8 fl oz)	warm water	1¹/₄ cups

1) Mix equal quantities of cider vinegar and molasses into the warm water (more or less than the amounts listed may be found more to taste).

2) Sip slowly for best benefits – this helps digestion and is beneficial for those on a cholesterol-controlled diet, according to old medicine traditions.

Dandelion Liquid

Dandelions have constituents which help liver function. The liver is intimately connected with cholesterol manufacture, storage and reprocessing and the drinking of 'dandelion water' helps the function of this vital organ. Dandelions are also rich in essential mineral salts including iron. The taste is bitter and this can be modified by using lemon juice as recommended in this recipe.

Serves 1

Metric (Imperial)		American
245 g (8 oz)	tender dandelion leaves	1 cup
425 ml (15 fl oz)	water	2 cups
pinch	sea salt (optional)	pinch
1 tbsp	fresh lemon juice	1 tbsp

1) Wash the dandelion leaves well and place into a saucepan with the water (add salt if desired).
2) Boil on a moderate heat for 30 minutes.
3) Drain the liquid, add 1 tablespoon of lemon juice and use this as a drink, warm or cold.

Ginger Tea

Ginger is an excellent soothing agent for digestive problems, it is also extremely useful in helping reduce cholesterol levels. Ginger tea is tasty but you need to discover for yourself the right amount to suit your taste. Experiment with the amount recommended and if not to your taste try a stronger brew next time.

Serves 2

Metric (Imperial)		American
1 tsp	freshly grated ginger	1 tsp
425 ml (15 fl oz)	boiling water	2 cups
1 tbsp	fresh lemon juice	1 tbsp
2 slices	lemon	2 slices

1) Place the grated ginger into a teapot and cover with boiling water. Leave to stand for 5 minutes.
2) Pour into mugs containing the lemon juice and add the slice of lemon.
3) Sip slowly as a delicious aid to digestion.

Cook's Note

The quantity of ginger used can be varied according to taste.

Keeping the ginger in the freezer makes it easier to grate and does not harm its flavour or efficacy.

Vegetable Cocktail

This mixture of juices contains a rich supply of mineral salts and should be slowly sipped, almost 'chewed', for maximum value.

Serves 1

Metric (Imperial)		American
1	fresh beetroot, diced and uncooked	1
2	carrots, diced	2
2	celery stalks, chopped	2
1	apple, diced	1
1 tbsp	lemon juice	1 tbsp

1) Put all of the ingredients except for the lemon into a juice extractor.
2) Pour resulting liquid into a tumbler, add lemon juice (and ice cubes if desired).
3) This makes a nourishing and refreshing summer drink.

Dairy-Free Fruity Milkshake

Serves 2

Metric (Imperial)		American
3 to 4	ripe apricots (or 1 mango)	3 to 4
3 tbsp	ripe seasonal berries	3 tbsp
300 ml (10 fl oz)	soya or rice milk	2 cups
1 tsp	honey (optional)	1 tsp
2	ice cubes	2

1) Depip the apricots and remove the skin (or remove flesh from mango).
2) Wash the berries thoroughly.
3) Place all of the ingredients into a blender and process until well mixed.
4) Add more ice cubes if desired.

Cook's Note

Available from any health store – ensure that the soya milk is unsweetened.

Index

Recipes

YOUR CONTROL CHOLESTEROL COOKBOOK